Contents

Chapter activities and answers

	Section 1: Accounts Preparation I	questions	answers
1	The accounting system	2	58
2	Double-entry book-keeping	6	60
3	Balancing accounts and the trial balance	12	66
4	Financial statements – the extended trial balance	18	73
5	Accruals and prepayments	21	76
6	Depreciation of non-current assets	25	79
7	Irrecoverable debts and allowance for doubtful debts	30	82
8	The rules of accounting	36	85
9	Accounting for capital transactions	41	89
10	Control accounts	45	93
11	The journal and correction of errors	50	95

Practice assessments and answers

Accounts preparation I Practice assessment 1	99	138
Accounts preparation I Practice assessment 2	111	144
Accounts preparation I Practice assessment 3	123	149

Acknowledgements

The publisher wishes to thank the following for their help with the reading and production of the book: Jean Cox, Maz Loton and Cathy Turner. Thanks are also due to Roger Petheram for his technical editorial work and to Laura Ingham for her designs for this series.

The publisher is indebted to the Association of Accounting Technicians for its kind permission for the reproduction of its sample assessment in this text.

Author

David Cox has more than twenty years' experience teaching accountancy students over a wide range of levels. Formerly with the Management and Professional Studies Department at Worcester College of Technology, he now lectures on a freelance basis and carries out educational consultancy work in accountancy studies. He is author and joint author of a number of textbooks in the areas of accounting, finance and banking.

Introduction

what this book covers

This book has been written specifically to cover the Learning Area 'Accounts Preparation I' which combines three QCF Units in the AAT Level 3 Diploma in Accounting:

- Principles of accounts preparation
- Extending the trial balance using accounting adjustments
- Accounting for fixed assets

what this book contains

This book is set out in two sections:

- **Chapter activities** which provide extra practice material in addition to the activities included in the Osborne Books Tutorial text. Answers to the Chapter activities are set out in this book.
- **Practice assessments** are included to prepare the student for the Computer Based Assessment. They are based directly on the structure, style and content of the sample assessment materials provided by the AAT at www.aat.org.uk. Suggested answers to the Practice Assessments are set out in this book.

online support from Osborne Books

This book is supported by practice material available at www.osbornebooks.co.uk

This material is available to tutors – and to students at their discretion – in two forms:

- A **Tutor Zone** which is available to tutors who have adopted the Osborne Books texts. This area of the website provides extra assessment practice material (plus answers) in addition to the activities included in this Workbook text.
- **Online learning** – online practice questions designed to familiarise students with the style of the AAT Computer Based Assessments.

  Scan the code on the right using your Smartphone to gain access to the online practice questions.

further information

If you want to know more about our products, please visit www.osbornebooks.co.uk, email books@osbornebooks.co.uk or telephone Osborne Books Customer Services on 01905 748071.

Chapter activities

1 Chapter activities
The accounting system

1.1 Fill in the missing words to the following sentences:

(a) The .... accountant is mainly concerned with external reporting.

(b) The sales day book is an example of a book of ....

(c) Sales ledger contains the personal accounts of ....

(d) Sales account is contained in the .... ledger.

(e) Income minus .... equals ....

(f) .... minus .... equals capital.

1.2 In an accounting system, which one of the following represents the most logical sequence?

	✔
book of prime entry; financial document; double-entry book-keeping; trial balance; financial statements (final accounts)	
financial document; book of prime entry; double-entry book-keeping; trial balance; financial statements (final accounts)	
financial document; book of prime entry; double-entry book-keeping; financial statements (final accounts); trial balance	
financial document; double-entry book-keeping, book of prime entry; trial balance; financial statements (final accounts)	

1.3 Write out the figures which make up the accounting equation (assets – liabilities = capital) after each of the following consecutive transactions (ignore VAT):

- owner starts in business with capital of £10,000 comprising £9,000 in the bank and £1,000 in cash

- purchases office equipment for £2,500, paying from the bank

- a friend lends £2,000, which is paid into the bank

- purchases machinery for £8,000, paying from the bank

- purchases office equipment for £2,000 on credit from Wyvern Office Supplies

1.4 Fill in the missing figures:

	Assets £	**Liabilities** £	**Capital** £
(a)	10,000	0	....
(b)	20,000	7,500	....
(c)	16,750	....	10,500
(d)	....	4,350	12,680
(e)	17,290	....	11,865
(f)	....	6,709	17,294

1.5 The table below sets out account balances from the books of a business. The columns (a) to (f) show the account balances resulting from a series of transactions that have taken place over time. You are to compare each set of adjacent columns, ie (a) with (b), (b) with (c), and so on, and state, with figures, what accounting transactions have taken place in each case. (Ignore VAT).

	(a)	(b)	(c)	(d)	(e)	(f)
	£	£	£	£	£	£
Assets						
Office equipment	–	5,000	5,000	5,500	5,500	5,500
Machinery	–	–	–	–	6,000	6,000
Bank	7,000	2,000	7,000	7,000	1,000	3,000
Cash	1,000	1,000	1,000	500	500	500
Liabilities						
Loan	–	–	5,000	5,000	5,000	5,000
Capital	8,000	8,000	8,000	8,000	8,000	10,000

2 Chapter activities Double-entry book-keeping

Note: a set of photocopiable blank ledger accounts is printed in the Appendix of *Sole trader and partnership accounts: tutorial*, and is also available in the Resources section of www.osbornebooks.co.uk.

2.1 Fill in the missing words to the following sentences:

(a) A .... entry records an account which gains value, or records an asset, or an expense.

(b) In the books of a business, the .... side of bank account records money paid out.

(c) In capital account, the initial capital contributed by the owner of the business is recorded on the .... side.

(d) Office equipment is an example of a .... asset.

(e) The purchase of a photocopier for use in the office is classed as .... expenditure.

(f) Repairs to a photocopier are classed as .... expenditure.

2.2 The following are the business transactions of Andrew King (who is not registered for VAT) for the month of October 20-4:

1 Oct	Started in business with capital of £7,500 in the bank
4 Oct	Purchased a machine for £4,000, paying by bank transfer (BACS)
6 Oct	Purchased office equipment for £2,250, paying by bank transfer
11 Oct	Paid rent £400, by bank transfer
12 Oct	Received a loan of £1,500 from a friend, Tina Richards, paid into the bank
15 Oct	Paid wages £500, by bank transfer
18 Oct	Commission received £200, by bank transfer
20 Oct	Drawings £250, by bank transfer
25 Oct	Paid wages £450, by bank transfer

You are to:

(a) write up Andrew King's bank account

(b) complete the double-entry book-keeping transactions

2.3 The purchase of goods for resale on credit is recorded in the accounts as:

Debit	*Credit*	✔
trade payables account	purchases account	
purchases account	cash account	
purchases account	trade payables account	
trade payables account	sales account	

Note: trade payable = creditor

2.4 Unsatisfactory goods, which were purchased on credit, are returned to the supplier. This is recorded in the accounts as:

Debit	*Credit*	✔
sales returns account	trade payables account	
purchases returns account	trade payables account	
trade payables account	purchases returns account	
trade payables account	purchases account	

Note: trade payable = creditor

2.5 For each transaction below, complete the table to show the accounts which will be debited and credited:

(a) Purchased goods, paying from the bank

(b) Payment received for cash sales, paid into the bank

(c) Purchased goods on credit from Teme Traders

(d) Sold goods on credit to L Harris

(e) Returned unsatisfactory goods to Teme Traders

(f) L Harris returns unsatisfactory goods

(g) Received a loan from D Perkins, paid into the bank

(h) Withdrew cash from the bank for use in the business

Note: ignore Value Added Tax

Transaction	Account debited	Account credited
(a)		
(b)		
(c)		
(d)		
(e)		
(f)		
(g)		
(h)		

2.6 The following are the business transactions of Pershore Packaging for the month of January 20-8:

4 Jan	Purchased goods, £250, on credit from AB Supplies Limited
5 Jan	Sold goods, £195, a bank transfer (BACS) received
7 Jan	Sold goods, £150, cash received
11 Jan	Received a loan of £1,000 from J Johnson, paid into the bank
15 Jan	Paid £250 to AB Supplies Limited by bank transfer
18 Jan	Sold goods, £145, on credit to L Lewis
20 Jan	Purchased goods, £225, paying by bank transfer
22 Jan	Paid wages, £125, in cash
26 Jan	Purchased office equipment, £160, on credit from Mercia Office Supplies Limited
28 Jan	Received a bank transfer for £145 from L Lewis
29 Jan	Paid the amount owing to Mercia Office Supplies Limited by bank transfer

You are to record the transactions in the books of account.

Notes:

- *Pershore Packaging is not registered for Value Added Tax*
- *day books are not required*

2.7 Enter the following transactions into the double-entry accounts of Sonya Smith:

20-6	
2 Feb	Purchased goods £200, on credit from G Lewis
4 Feb	Sold goods £150, on credit to L Jarvis
8 Feb	Sold goods £240, on credit to G Patel
10 Feb	Paid G Lewis the amount owing by bank transfer after deducting a settlement discount of 5%
12 Feb	L Jarvis pays the amount owing by bank transfer after deducting a settlement discount of 2%
17 Feb	Purchased goods £160, on credit from G Lewis
19 Feb	G Patel pays the amount owing by bank transfer after deducting a settlement discount of 2.5%
24 Feb	Paid G Lewis the amount owing by bank transfer after deducting a settlement discount of 5%

Notes:

- *Sonya Smith is not registered for Value Added Tax*
- *day books are not required*

3 Chapter activities
Balancing accounts and the trial balance

Note: a set of photocopiable blank ledger accounts is printed in the Appendix of *Sole trader and partnership accounts: tutorial,* and is also available in the Resources section of www.osbornebooks.co.uk.

3.1 Which one of the following accounts normally has a debit balance?

	✔
loan	
bank overdraft	
sales	
purchases	

3.2 Which one of the following accounts normally has a credit balance?

	✔
drawings	
capital	
cash	
premises	

3.3 Prepare the trial balance of Tina Wong as at 30 November 20-9. You are to fill in the missing figure for her capital in order to balance the trial balance.

	£
Bank overdraft	1,855
Capital	?
Cash	85
Office equipment	2,500
Purchases	2,419
Purchases returns	102
Sales	4,164
Sales returns	354
Trade payables (creditors)	1,082
Trade receivables (debtors)	2,115
Vehicle	7,500
Wages	1,230

3.4 The book-keeper of Lorna Fox has extracted the following list of balances as at 31 March 20-1:

	£
Administration expenses	10,240
Bank overdraft	1,050
Capital	155,440
Cash	150
Drawings	9,450
Interest paid	2,350
Loan from bank	20,000
Machinery	40,000
Premises	125,000
Purchases	96,250
Sales	146,390
Sales returns	8,500
Telephone	3,020
Trade payables (creditors)	10,545
Trade receivables (debtors)	10,390
Travel expenses	1,045
Value Added Tax (amount due to HM Revenue and Customs)	1,950
Wages	28,980

You are to:

(a) Produce the trial balance at 31 March 20-1.

(b) Take any three debit balances and any three credit balances and explain to someone who does not understand accounting why they are listed as such, and what this means to the business.

3.5 Fill in the missing words to the following sentences:

(a) "You made an error of .... when you debited the cost of diesel fuel for the van to Vans Account."

(b) "There is a 'bad figure' on a purchases invoice – we have read it as £35 when it should be £55. It has gone through our accounts wrongly so we have an error of .... to put right."

(c) "Who was in charge of that trainee last week? He has entered the payment for the electricity bill on the debit side of the bank and on the credit side of electricity – a .... of ...."

(d) "I found this purchase invoice from last week in amongst the copy statements. As we haven't put it through the accounts we have an error of ...."

(e) "I've had the book-keeper from D Jones Limited on the 'phone concerning the statements of account that we sent out the other day. She says that there is a sales invoice charged that she knows nothing about. I wonder if we have done a .... and it should be for T Jones' account?"

(f) "Although the trial balance balanced last week, I've since found an error of £100 in the calculation of the balance of sales account. We will need to check the other balances as I think we may have a .... error."

3.6 The following are the business transactions of Mark Tansall, a retailer of computer software, for the months of January and February 20-4:

Transactions for January

20-4	
1 Jan	Started in business with capital of £10,000 in the bank
4 Jan	Paid rent on premises £500, by bank transfer (BACS)
5 Jan	Purchased shop fittings £5,000, paid by bank transfer
7 Jan	Purchased stock of software, £7,500, on credit from Tech Software
11 Jan	Software sales £2,400, paid into bank
12 Jan	Software sales £2,000, paid into bank
16 Jan	Purchased software £5,000, on credit from Datasoft Limited
20 Jan	Software sales £1,500 to Wyvern School, a bank transfer received
22 Jan	Software sales £2,250, paid into bank
25 Jan	Purchased software from A & A Supplies £3,000, paid by bank transfer
27 Jan	Wyvern School returned software £280, refund made by bank transfer
29 Jan	Sold software on credit to Teme College, £2,495

Transactions for February

20-4	
2 Feb	Software sales £2,720, paid into bank
4 Feb	Paid rent on premises £500, by bank transfer
5 Feb	Purchased shop fittings £1,550, paid by bank transfer
10 Feb	Software sales £3,995, paid into bank
12 Feb	Bank transfer, £7,500, to Tech Software
15 Feb	Purchased software £4,510, on credit from Tech Software
19 Feb	Bank transfer, £5,000, to Datasoft Limited
22 Feb	Software sales £1,930, paid into bank
23 Feb	Teme College returned software, £145
24 Feb	Software sales £2,145, paid into bank
25 Feb	Purchased software £2,120, on credit from Associated Software
26 Feb	Software sales £4,150, paid into bank

You are to:

(a) Record the January transactions in the books of account, and balance each account at 31 January 20-4.

(b) Draw up a trial balance at 31 January 20-4.

(c) Record the February transactions in the books of account, and balance each account at 28 February 20-4.

(d) Draw up a trial balance at 28 February 20-4.

Notes:

- *Mark Tansall is not registered for Value Added Tax*
- *day books are not required*
- *Mark Tansall's accounting system does not use control accounts*
- *make sure that you leave plenty of space for each account – particularly sales, purchases and bank*

4 Chapter activities
Financial statements – the extended trial balance

Extended trial balance format

A blank photocopiable extended trial balance is included in the Appendix of *Sole trader and partnership accounts: tutorial*, and is also available in the Resources section of www.osbornebooks.co.uk. It is advisable to enlarge it up to full A4 size. Alternatively you can set up a computer spreadsheet – but remember to allow for all the rows shown on the layout – they will be needed in later Workbook activities.

4.1 Which one of the following does not appear in the income statement?

	✔
closing inventory (stock)	
purchases	
interest paid	
cash	

4.2 Which one of the following does not appear in the statement of financial position?

	✔
closing inventory (stock)	
sales revenue	
trade receivables (debtors)	
bank	

4.3 The following trial balance has been extracted by Matt Smith at 31 December 20-3:

	Dr	*Cr*
	£	£
Opening inventory	14,350	
Purchases	114,472	
Sales revenue		259,688
Rent and rates	13,718	
Heating and lighting	12,540	
Wages and salaries	42,614	
Vehicle expenses	5,817	
Advertising	6,341	
Premises at cost	75,000	
Office equipment at cost	33,000	
Vehicles at cost	21,500	
Sales ledger control (receivables)	23,854	
Bank	1,235	
Cash	125	
Capital		62,500
Drawings	12,358	
Loan from bank		35,000
Purchases ledger control (payables)		14,258
Value Added Tax		5,478
Closing inventory – income statement		16,280
Closing inventory – statement of financial position	16,280	
	393,204	393,204

You are to prepare the extended trial balance of Matt Smith for the year ended 31 December 20-3.

4.4 The following trial balance has been extracted by Clare Lewis at 31 December 20-4:

	Dr	Cr
	£	£
Sales ledger control (receivables)	18,600	
Purchases ledger control (payables)		11,480
Value Added Tax		1,870
Bank		4,610
Capital		25,250
Sales revenue		144,810
Purchases	96,318	
Opening inventory	16,010	
Salaries	18,465	
Heating and lighting	1,820	
Rent and rates	5,647	
Vehicles at cost	9,820	
Office equipment at cost	5,500	
Sundry expenses	845	
Vehicle expenses	1,684	
Drawings	13,311	
Closing inventory – income statement		13,735
Closing inventory – statement of financial position	13,735	
	201,755	201,755

You are to prepare the extended trial balance of Clare Lewis for the year ended 31 December 20-4.

5 Chapter activities Accruals and prepayments

Extended trial balance format

A blank photocopiable extended trial balance is included in the Appendix of *Sole trader and partnership accounts: tutorial*, and is also available at www.osbornebooks.co.uk. It is advisable to enlarge it up to full A4 size. Alternatively you can set up a computer spreadsheet – but remember to allow for all the rows shown on the layout – they will be needed in later Workbook activities.

5.1 A credit balance brought down at the start of the year on an expenses account indicates:

	✔
a liability and an expense accrued	
an asset and an expense prepaid	
an asset and an expense accrued	
a liability and an expense prepaid	

5.2 Which one of the following is an asset?

	✔
trade payables	
wages accrued	
bank overdraft	
vehicle expenses prepaid	

5.3 This Activity is about accounting for accruals and prepayments and preparing a trial balance.

You are working on the accounts of a business for the year ended 31 March 20-2. In this Activity you can ignore VAT.

You have the following information:

Balances as at:	**1 April 20-1** **£**
Accrual for selling expenses	400
Prepayment for vehicle expenses	150

The bank summary for the year shows payments for selling expenses of £12,700. Included in this figure is £1,650 for the quarter ended 30 April 20-2.

(a) **You are to** prepare the selling expenses account for the year ended 31 March 20-2 and close it off by showing the transfer to the income statement. Dates are not required.

Selling expenses

	£		£

The bank summary for the year shows payments for vehicle expenses of £7,200. In April 20-2, £280 was paid for vehicle expenses incurred in March 20-2.

(b) **You are to** prepare the vehicle expenses account for the year ended 31 March 20-2 and close it off by showing the transfer to the income statement. Include dates.

Vehicle expenses

		£			£

You have the following extract of balances from the general ledger.

(c) **Using your answers** to (a) and (b), and the figures given below, enter amounts in the appropriate debit or credit column for the accounts shown. Do not enter zeros in unused column cells.

Extract from trial balance as at 31 March 20-2

Account	£	£ Dr	£ Cr
Accruals			
Capital	45,000		
Discount allowed	470		
Drawings	12,500		
Interest paid	380		
Office equipment at cost	24,500		
Prepayments			
Purchases returns	2,740		

5.4 The following trial balance has been extracted by Cindy Hayward, who runs a delicatessen shop, at 30 June 20-4:

	Dr £	*Cr* £
Capital		90,932
Drawings	10,000	
Purchases	148,500	
Sales revenue		210,900
Repairs to buildings	848	
Vehicles at cost	15,000	
Vehicle expenses	1,540	
Land and buildings at cost	185,000	
Loan from bank		110,000
Bank	540	
Shop fittings at cost	12,560	
Wages	30,280	
Discount allowed	135	
Discount received		1,319
Rates and insurance	2,690	
Sales ledger control	3,175	
Purchases ledger control		8,295
Heating and lighting	3,164	
General expenses	4,680	
Sales returns	855	
Purchases returns		1,221
Opening inventory	6,210	
Value Added Tax		2,510
Closing inventory – income statement		7,515
Closing inventory – statement of financial position	7,515	
	432,692	432,692

Notes at 30 June 20-4:

- rates prepaid £255
- wages owing £560
- vehicle expenses owing £85
- goods costing £200 were taken by Cindy Hayward for her own use

You are to prepare the extended trial balance of Cindy Hayward for the year ended 30 June 20-4.

6 Chapter activities
Depreciation of non-current assets

Extended trial balance format

A blank photocopiable extended trial balance is included in the Appendix of *Sole trader and partnership accounts: tutorial*, and is also available in the Resources section of www.osbornebooks.co.uk. It is advisable to enlarge it up to full A4 size. Alternatively you can set up a computer spreadsheet – but remember to allow for all the rows shown on the layout – they will be needed in later Workbook activities.

6.1 A car which cost £20,000 is being depreciated at 30 per cent per year using the reducing (diminishing) balance method. At the end of three years it will have a carrying amount (net book value) of:

	✔
£2,000	
£6,860	
£13,140	
£18,000	

6.2 A car is being depreciated using the reducing (diminishing) balance method. The original cost of the car was £15,000. At the end of year three it has a carrying amount (net book value) of £5,145. What percentage of reducing balance is being used?

	✔
20%	
25%	
30%	
35%	

6.3 A machine which originally cost £1,000 is sold for £350 (both amounts net of VAT). The machinery: accumulated depreciation account shows a balance of £620. This means that there is a:

	✔
loss on disposal of £380	
profit on disposal of £350	
loss on disposal of £30	
profit on disposal of £30	

6.4 The book-keeping entries to record a profit on disposal of non-current assets are:

Debit	*Credit*	✔
non-current asset account	income statement	
disposals account	income statement	
income statement	disposals account	
bank account	income statement	

6.5 This Activity is about recording non-current asset information in the general ledger.

- You are working on the accounts of a business that is registered for VAT.
- During the year an old machine was disposed.
- The machine had been bought for £8,000 plus VAT (the VAT was reclaimed).
- Two years' depreciation has been applied.
- Depreciation is provided at 20 per cent per year on a reducing balance basis.
- The machine was sold for £4,800 plus VAT (at 20%), with payment being received into the bank.

You are to:

(a) Calculate the accumulated depreciation on the machine now sold:

year 1	£
year 2	£
total	£

(b) Make entries in the accounts which follow to record the disposal of the machine, showing clearly any balance carried down or transferred to the income statement.

Machine at cost

Balance b/d	£8,000		

Machine: disposals

Bank

(c) Tick the relevant box to show whether there is a profit or loss on disposal of the machine

profit	
loss	

6.6 The following trial balance has been extracted by the book-keeper of Wintergreen Supplies at 31 December 20-6:

	Dr	*Cr*
	£	£
Premises at cost	120,000	
Premises: accumulated depreciation		7,200
Bank loan		52,800
Capital		70,000
Sales ledger control	11,900	
Purchases ledger control		11,500
Drawings	6,750	
Cash	150	
Opening inventory	4,200	
Office equipment at cost	5,000	
Office equipment: accumulated depreciation		1,000
Vehicles at cost	10,000	
Vehicles: accumulated depreciation		2,000
Bank		750
Sales revenue		194,850
Purchases	154,000	
Wages	20,500	
Sundry expenses	9,500	
Value Added Tax		1,750
Disposal of non-current asset		150
Closing inventory – income statement		5,200
Closing inventory – statement of financial position	5,200	
	347,200	347,200

Notes at 31 December 20-6:

- depreciate premises at 2 per cent using the straight-line method
- depreciate vehicles and office equipment at 20 per cent using the straight-line method
- wages prepaid are £560, and sundry expenses accrued are £500

You are to prepare the extended trial of Wintergreen Supplies for the year ended 31 December 20-6.

7 Chapter activities
Irrecoverable debts and allowance for doubtful debts

Extended trial balance format

A blank photocopiable extended trial balance is included in the Appendix of *Sole trader and partnership accounts: tutorial*, and is also available in the Resources section of www.osbornebooks.co.uk. It is advisable to enlarge it up to full A4 size. Alternatively you can set up a computer spreadsheet – but remember to allow for all the rows shown on the layout – they will be needed in later Workbook activities.

7.1 The accounts supervisor of the firm where you work has instructed you to write off the receivable (debtors) account of T Neal as irrecoverable. Which one of the following entries will you make in the double-entry accounts (assume that the business does not use control accounts)?

Debit	*Credit*	✔
T Neal's account	irrecoverable debts account	
bank account	T Neal's account	
irrecoverable debts account	T Neal's account	
T Neal's account	allowance for doubtful debts account	

Note: ignore VAT

7.2 An increase in the allowance for doubtful debts will:

	✔
decrease profit for the year	
be recorded in the receivables accounts in sales ledger	
decrease the bank balance	
increase profit for the year	

7.3 The income statement of a business has been prepared showing a loss for the year of £2,350. A reduction of £150 in the allowance for doubtful debts should have been made, and irrecoverable debts of £70 should have been written off. Loss for the year will now be:

	✔
£2,130	
£2,270	
£2,430	
£2,570	

Note: ignore VAT

7.4 You are the book-keeper at Enterprise Trading Company. The following information is available for the financial years ending 31 December 20-5, 20-6, 20-7:

	£
• Receivables balances at 31 December 20-5, before writing off irrecoverable debts	105,200
• Irrecoverable debts written off on 31 December 20-5	1,800
• 2.5% allowance for doubtful debts created at 31 December 20-5	
• Receivables balances at 31 December 20-6, before writing off irrecoverable debts	115,600
• Irrecoverable debts written off on 31 December 20-6	2,400
• 2.5% allowance for doubtful debts adjusted in line with the change in the level of receivables at 31 December 20-6	
• Receivables balances at 31 December 20-7, before writing off irrecoverable debts	110,200
• Irrecoverable debts written off on 31 December 20-7	1,400
• 2.5% allowance for doubtful debts adjusted in line with the change in the level of receivables at 31 December 20-7	

Note: ignore VAT

You are to show the effect of the above transactions on the financial statements in the following table:

Year	**Income statement**			**Statement of financial position**	
	Dr *irrecoverable debts* £	Dr *allowance for doubtful debts: adjustment* £	Cr *allowance for doubtful debts: adjustment* £	Dr *sales ledger control (receivables)* £	Cr *allowance for doubtful debts* £
20-5					
20-6					
20-7					

7.5 This Activity is about accounting for irrecoverable debts and allowance for doubtful debts and preparing a trial balance.

You are working on the financial statements of a business for the year ended 31 December 20-6. In this task you can ignore VAT.

You have the following information:

Irrecoverable debts to be written off:	£
Craven Traders	75
Harris and Co	110
P Mahon	55
Allowance for doubtful debts at 1 January 20-6	300

The balance of trade receivables (sales ledger control account) before irrecoverable debts are written off is £12,740. The allowance for doubtful debts is to be 2% of trade receivables after irrecoverable debts.

(a) **You are to** prepare the irrecoverable debts account for the year ended 31 December 20-6 and close it off by showing the transfer to the income statement. Dates are not required.

Irrecoverable debts

	£		£

(b) **You are to** prepare the allowance for doubtful debts account for the year ended 31 December 20-6 and to show clearly the balance carried down. Include dates.

Allowance for doubtful debts

		£			£

You have the following extract of balances from the general ledger.

(c) **Using your answers** from (a) and (b), record the adjustments on the extract from the extended trial balance. Do not enter zeros in unused column cells.

Extract from trial balance as at 31 December 20-6

Account	**Ledger balances**		**Adjustments**	
	Dr £	**Cr £**	**Dr £**	**Cr £**
Allowance for doubtful debts		300		
Allowance for doubtful debts: adjustment				
Irrecoverable debts				
Purchases ledger control		8,960		
Sales ledger control	12,740			
Vehicles at cost	20,000			
Vehicles: accumulated depreciation		11,200		
Wages	22,850			

7.6 The following trial balance has been extracted by the book-keeper of Jane Jones, who sells carpets, as at 31 December 20-5:

	Dr £	*Cr* £
Sales ledger control	37,200	
Purchases ledger control		30,640
Value Added Tax		4,280
Bank	14,640	
Capital		50,500
Sales revenue		289,620
Purchases	182,636	
Opening inventory	32,020	
Wages and salaries	36,930	
Heat and light	3,640	
Rent and rates	11,294	
Vehicles at cost	20,000	
Vehicles: accumulated depreciation		4,000
Machinery at cost	10,000	
Machinery: accumulated depreciation		1,000
Sundry expenses	1,690	
Vehicle expenses	3,368	
Drawings	26,622	
Closing inventory – income statement		34,000
Closing inventory – statement of financial position	34,000	
	414,040	414,040

Notes at 31 December 20-5:

- irrecoverable debts of £2,200 are to be written off and an allowance for doubtful debts of 5% is to be created
- depreciate vehicles at 20% per annum and machinery at 10% per annum, using the reducing balance method
- there are sundry expenses accruals of £270, and rates prepayments of £2,190

You are to prepare the extended trial balance of Jane Jones for the year ended 31 December 20-5.

8 Chapter activities The rules of accounting

8.1 (a) Explain the accounting concept of materiality.

(b) Describe three types of situation to which the concept of materiality is applicable.

8.2 Eveshore Electronics Limited imports electronic goods from the Far East and sells to retailers in the UK. The company has always valued its inventory on the FIFO (first in, first out) method. One of the directors comments that, because of the recent strength of the pound sterling against Far Eastern currencies, the price of imported electronic goods has been falling throughout the year. She suggests that the closing inventory should be recalculated on the LIFO (last in, first out) method.

(a) Assuming that the price of electronic goods has been falling throughout the year, would the change

	✔
increase profit for the year	
decrease profit for the year	
have no effect on profit for the year	

(b) "A business should not normally change its basis for valuing inventory unless it has good reasons for so doing." Which accounting concept supports this statement?

	✔
business entity	
materiality	
going concern	
accruals	
prudence	
consistency	

8.3 (a) IAS 2 *Inventories* states that inventories are to be valued at ....

.... (complete the sentence).

(b) A business buys twenty units of a product in January at a cost of £3.00 each; it buys ten more in February at £3.50 each, and ten in April at £4.00 each. Eight units are sold in March, and sixteen are sold in May.

What is the value of the closing inventory at the end of May using FIFO (first in, first out) and LIFO (last in, first out)?

	FIFO ✔	**LIFO** ✔
£54		
£61		
£60		
£48		
£40		
£135		

8.4 YZ Limited is formed on 1 January 20-4 and trades in two products, Y and Z. At the end of its first half year the inventory movements of the two products are as follows:

20-4	**PRODUCT Y**		**PRODUCT Z**	
	Bought (units)	Sold (units)	Bought (units)	Sold (units)
January	100 at £4.00		200 at £10.00	
February		80 at £10.00	100 at £9.50	
March	140 at £4.20			240 at £16.00
April	100 at £3.80		100 at £10.50	
May		140 at £10.00	140 at £10.00	
June	80 at £4.50			100 at £16.00

The company values inventory on the FIFO (first in, first out) method.

At 30 June 20-4, the net realisable value of each type of inventory is:

product Y	£1,750.00
product Z	£1,950.00
	£3,700.00

You are to calculate the value of:

(a) sales revenue for the half year

(b) closing inventory valuation at 30 June 20-4 for each product using the FIFO basis

(c) amount at which the company's inventories should be valued on 30 June 20-4 in order to comply with IAS 2 *Inventories*

(d) cost of sales for the half year in order to comply with IAS 2 *Inventories*

8.5 Which one of the following is revenue expenditure?

	✔
purchase of a computer for the office	
legal costs for the purchase of property	
cost of extension to property	
quarterly electricity bill	

8.6 Which one of the following is capital expenditure?

	✔
repairs to vehicles	
goods taken by owner for own use	
cost of materials used to extend the premises	
renewing the electrical wiring in the office	

8.7 Wages paid to own employees who have redecorated the office are:

	✔
capital expenditure	
debited to the income statement	
debited to premises account	
credited to the income statement	

8.8 Classify the following costs:

	capital expenditure ✔	revenue expenditure ✔
(a) purchase of vehicles		
(b) depreciation of vehicles		
(c) rent paid on premises		
(d) wages and salaries		
(e) legal fees relating to the purchase of property		
(f) redecoration of office		
(g) installation of air-conditioning in office		
(h) wages of own employees used to build extension to the office		
(i) installation and setting up of a new machine		

9 Chapter activities
Accounting for capital transactions

9.1 Which one of the following is an intangible non-current asset?

	✔
vehicles	
goodwill	
hire purchase	
premises	

9.2 Eveshore Enterprises is considering the use of hire purchase as a means of financing a new computer. Which of the following statements is correct?

	✔
at the end of the hire purchase period, ownership of the computer will be transferred from the finance company to Eveshore Enterprises	
a hire purchase agreement is the same as a finance lease	
at the end of the hire purchase period, the finance company will collect the computer from Eveshore Enterprises	
Eveshore Enterprises will have ownership of the computer from the start of the hire purchase period	

9.3 John and Sara Smith run a delivery company called 'J & S Transport'. They started in business on 1 January 20-2 with two vans which cost £16,000 each (paid from the bank). On 1 January 20-4, a further two vans were bought at a cost of £18,000 each (paid from the bank) and, on 20 March 20-4, one of the original vans was sold for £8,000 (paid into the bank).

Depreciation is charged at 25 per cent each year, using the reducing balance method; depreciation is charged in the year of purchase, but not in the year of disposal.

The Smith's financial year end is 31 December.

You are to show the accounting entries (journal and cash book not required) to record the acquisition, depreciation and disposal of vans for the years 20-2, 20-3 and 20-4.

Notes:

- VAT is to be ignored
- use one non-current asset vehicles account for all vans, one depreciation charge account and one vehicles: accumulated depreciation account

9.4 Jane Barnet runs a printing business called 'Speedprint'. She needs to buy a replacement printing machine at a cost of £60,000 – the old machine is worn out and is worth only £500 as scrap.

Speedprint's current summary statement of financial position is as follows:

	£
Non-current assets	150,000
Current assets	80,000
	230,000
Less Current liabilities (including bank)	75,000
	155,000
Less Non-current liabilities	40,000
NET ASSETS	115,000
Capital	115,000

Speedprint is a profitable business, but one that is short of cash – the bank overdraft is up to the limit and Jane does not wish to approach the bank to seek an increase in the limit. The non-current liabilities are loans from friends and relatives – Jane does not wish to ask them for further monies.

Suggest TWO possible funding mathods that Jane should consider to finance the new printing machine. Briefly summarise the features of each funding method.

9.5 This Activity is about recording information for non-current assets for a business known as Marston Metals. Marston Metals is registered for VAT.

The following is a purchase invoice received by Marston Metals:

To: Marston Metals Unit 10, Sunnydale Estate Marston MR3 8JK	**Invoice 4728** Machine Supplies plc Wyvern Road Eveshore EV2 1QL		**Date:** 17 June 20-5
Pressing machine	Reference AB347	1	2,500.00
Installation of machine		1	160.00
One year service contract		1	100.00
VAT @ 20%			552.00
Total			3,312.00
Settlement terms: strictly 30 days net			

The following information relates to the sale of a van:

Registration number	AB03 TPJ
Date of sale	14 February 20-6
Selling price	£8,000.00

- Marston Metals has a policy of capitalising expenditure over £500.
- Vehicles are depreciated at 25% on a reducing balance basis.
- Machinery is depreciated at 20% on a straight-line basis assuming no residual value.
- Non-current assets are depreciated in the year of acquisition but not in the year of disposal.

Record the following information in the non-current asset register on the next page.

(a) Any acquisitions of non-current assets during the year ended 31 March 20-6

(b) Any disposals of non-current assets during the year ended 31 March 20-6

(c) Depreciation for the year ended 31 March 20-6

NON-CURRENT ASSET REGISTER

Description/serial no	Acquisition date	Cost £	Depreciation £	Carrying amount £	Funding method	Disposal proceeds £	Disposal date
Machinery							
Moulding machine	12/08/-3	10,000.00			Cash		
Year end 31/03/-4			2,000.00	8,000.00			
Year end 31/03/-5			2,000.00	6,000.00			
Year end 31/03/-6							
Year end 31/03/-6							
Vehicles							
AB03 TPJ	11/06/-3	16,400.00			Cash		
Year end 31/03/-4			4,100.00	12,300.00			
Year end 31/03/-5			3,075.00	9,225.00			
Year end 31/03/-6							
AB54 PZE	01/01/-5	15,200.00			Part-exchange		
Year end 31/03/-5			3,800.00	11,400.00			
Year end 31/03/-6							

10 Chapter activities
Control accounts

10.1 Indicate whether the following errors would cause a difference between the balance of the sales ledger control account and the total of the balances in the sales ledger.

Error	Difference ✔	No difference ✔
Sales returns day book was undercast by £100.		
A credit note for £75 was credited to the account of Martley Traders instead of Martley Manufacturing – both are sales ledger accounts.		
The sales ledger account of C Fernandez, £125, has been written off as irrecoverable, but no entry has been made in sales ledger control account.		
A set-off entry for £45 has been incorrectly recorded as £54 in the sales ledger control account and in the sales ledger account.		

10.2 On 31 December 20-6 the balances of the trade payables accounts in the purchases ledger of Thomas Limited were listed, totalled, and compared with the balance of the purchases ledger control account. The total of the list of purchases ledger balances amounted to £55,946. Investigations were carried out and the following errors were discovered:

(a) a purchases ledger balance of £553 had been listed as £535

(b) settlement (cash) discount received of £100 had been credited to the trade payables account

(c) a credit note received for £141 had not been recorded in the trade payables account

(d) a purchases ledger balance of £225 had been listed twice

You are to record the appropriate adjustments in the table below; show clearly the amount involved and whether it is to be added or subtracted.

		£
Total of list of purchases ledger balances		55,946
Adjustment for (a)	add/subtract	....
Adjustment for (b)	add/subtract	....
Adjustment for (c)	add/subtract	....
Adjustment for (d)	add/subtract	....
Revised total to agree with purchases ledger control account		....

10.3 This Activity is about preparing reconciliations.

The sales ledger has been compared with sales ledger control account and the following differences identified:

1. Settlement (cash) discount of £120 allowed to trade receivables and entered in their sales ledger accounts has not been entered in sales ledger control account.

2. A set-off entry for £220 has been credited to the sales ledger account of Barker Limited instead of to the sales ledger account of Baker Limited.

3. In the cash book, the column for receipts from trade receivables has been undercast (underadded) by £100.

4. The account of D Doherty, £95, has been written off as irrecoverable in sales ledger, but has not been recorded in sales ledger control account.

The total of the account balances in sales ledger is £24,275 debit and the balance of sales ledger control account is £24,590 debit.

Use the following table to show the three adjustments you need to make to sales ledger control account.

Adjustment number	**Amount £**	**Debit ✓**	**Credit ✓**

10.4 This Activity is about preparing reconciliations.

The purchases ledger has been compared with purchases ledger control account and the following differences identified:

1. The total column of purchases day book has been undercast (underadded) by £500.
2. A set-off entry for £190 has been omitted from purchases ledger control account.
3. A purchases return of £240 has been debited to the purchases ledger account of Spence Limited instead of the purchases ledger account of Spencer Limited.
4. Settlement (cash) discount of £140 received from trade payables has been entered on the wrong side of purchases ledger control account.

The total of the account balances in purchases ledger is £18,790 credit and the balance of purchases ledger control account is £18,760 credit.

Use the following table to show the three adjustments you need to make to purchases ledger control account.

Adjustment number	**Amount £**	**Debit ✓**	**Credit ✓**

10.5 This Activity is about preparing reconciliations.

The bank statement has been compared with the bank columns of the cash book and the following differences identified:

1. Cheques totalling £1,210 paid into the bank yesterday are not showing on the bank statement.
2. A direct debit payment made by the bank for £360 has not been entered in the cash book.
3. A BACS receipt from a customer for £230 has been incorrectly entered in the cash book as £320.
4. Bank charges and interest of £120 have not been entered in the cash book.

The balance showing on the bank statement is a credit of £2,760 and the balance in the cash book is a debit of £4,540.

Use the following table to show the three adjustments you need to make to the cash book.

Adjustment number	**Amount £**	**Debit ✓**	**Credit ✓**

11 Chapter activities The journal and correction of errors

11.1 Which one of the following will not be recorded in the journal?

	✔
an irrecoverable debt written off	
correction of an error of omission	
closing inventory valuation at the year end	
bank payment to a trade payable	

11.2 The purchase of stationery, £25, has been debited in error to office equipment account. Which one of the following journal entries will correct the error?

Debit		*Credit*		✔
Office equipment	£25	Stationery	£25	
Suspense	£25	Office equipment	£25	
Stationery	£25	Office equipment	£25	
Stationery	£25	Suspense	£25	

Note: ignore VAT

11.3 A trial balance fails to agree by £27 and the difference is placed to a suspense account. Later it is found that a payment for vehicle repairs of £63 has been entered in the vehicle repairs account as £36. Which one of the following journal entries will correct the error?

Debit		*Credit*		✔
Suspense Vehicle repairs	£36 £63	Vehicle repairs Suspense	£36 £63	
Suspense	£27	Vehicle repairs	£27	
Vehicle repairs	£27	Bank	£27	
Vehicle repairs Suspense	£36 £63	Suspense Vehicle repairs	£36 £63	

Note: ignore VAT

11.4 What is the effect on the previously reported profit for the year of making each of the following adjustments?

Adjustment	**Profit increases ✔**	**Profit decreases ✔**
sales account has been overcast		
closing inventory has been undervalued		
telephone expenses account has been undercast		
discount received has been omitted		
depreciation charge for vehicles has been omitted		
a trade receivable account is written off as irrecoverable		
a reduction in the allowance for doubtful debts is made		

11.5 This Activity is about recording journal entries.

You are working on the financial statements of a business with a year end of 31 March. A trial balance has been drawn up and a suspense account opened with a debit balance of £5,840. You now need to make some corrections and adjustments for the year ended 31 March 20-2.

Record the journal entries needed in the general ledger to deal with the items below. You should:

- remove any incorrect entries, where appropriate
- post the correct entries

You do not need to give narratives.

Do NOT enter zeros into unused column cells.

Ignore VAT.

(a) Entries need to be made for an irrecoverable debt of £300.

Journal

	Dr **£**	**Cr** **£**

(b) A purchase of office equipment for £4,000 has been made from the bank. The correct entry was made to the bank account, but no other entries were made.

Journal

	Dr **£**	**Cr** **£**

(c) **No entries have been made for closing inventory for the year end 31 March 20-2. Closing inventory has been valued at cost at £18,380. Included in this figure are some items costing £940 that will be sold for £700.**

Journal

	Dr **£**	**Cr** **£**

(d) **The figures from the columns of the purchases day book for 31 March have been totalled correctly as follows:**

Purchases column	£4,600
VAT column	£920
Total column	£5,520

The amounts have been posted as follows:

Dr Purchases	£4,600
Cr VAT	£920
Cr Purchases ledger control	£5,520

Journal

	Dr **£**	**Cr** **£**

11.6 This Activity is about completing an extended balance.

You have the following extended trial balance. The adjustments have already been correctly entered.

Extend the figures into the income statement and statement of financial position.

Do NOT enter zeros into unused column cells.

Make the columns balance by entering figures in the correct places.

Extended trial balance

Ledger account	Ledger balances		Adjustments		Income statement		Statement of financial position	
	£ Dr	£ Cr	£ Dr	£ Cr	£ Dr	£ Cr	£ Dr	£ Cr
Allowance for doubtful debts		1,200	100					
Allowance for doubtful debts adjustment				100				
Bank	15,300							
Capital		30,000						
Closing inventory			25,230	25,230				
Depreciation charge			2,500					
Office equipment at cost	20,000							
Office equipment: accumulated depreciation		8,500		2,500				
Office expenses	12,700		500					
Opening inventory	22,680							
Payroll expenses	25,920			350				
Purchases	85,500		400					
Purchases ledger control		25,270						
Rent and rates	5,400			250				
Sales		151,200						
Sales ledger control	30,380							
Suspense	300		600	900				
VAT		2,010						
Profit/loss for the year								
	218,180	218,180	29,330	29,330				

Answers to chapter activities

1 Chapter activities – answers The accounting system

1.1 (a) The *financial* accountant is mainly concerned with external reporting.

(b) The sales day book is an example of a book of *prime entry.*

(c) Sales ledger contains the personal accounts of *receivables (debtors).*

(d) Sales account is contained in the *general* ledger.

(e) Income minus *expenses* equals *profit or loss.*

(f) *Assets* minus *liabilities* equals capital.

1.2 financial document; book of prime entry; double-entry book-keeping; trial balance; financial statements (final accounts)

1.3

- asset of bank increases by £9,000
  asset of cash increases by £1,000
  capital increases by £10,000
  assets £10,000 – liabilities £0 = capital £10,000

- asset of office equipment increases by £2,500
  asset of bank decreases by £2,500
  assets £10,000 – liabilities £0 = capital £10,000

- asset of bank increases by £2,000
  liability of loan increases by £2,000
  assets £12,000 – liabilities £2,000 = capital £10,000

- asset of machinery increases by £8,000
  asset of bank decreases by £8,000
  assets £12,000 – liabilities £2,000 = capital £10,000

- asset of office equipment increases by £2,000
  liabilities of payables (creditors) increases by £2,000
  assets £14,000 – liabilities £4,000 = capital £10,000

1.4

	Assets £	**Liabilities** £	**Capital** £
(a)	10,000	0	*10,000*
(b)	20,000	7,500	*12,500*
(c)	16,750	*6,250*	10,500
(d)	*17,030*	4,350	12,680
(e)	17,290	*5,425*	11,865
(f)	*24,003*	6,709	17,294

1.5 (a) Owner starts in business with capital of £8,000, comprising £7,000 in the bank and £1,000 in cash

(b) Purchases office equipment for £5,000, paying from the bank

(c) Receives a loan of £5,000, paid into the bank

(d) Purchases office equipment for £500, paying in cash

(e) Purchases machinery for £6,000, paying from the bank

(f) Owner introduces £2,000 additional capital, paid into the bank

2 Chapter activities – answers Double-entry book-keeping

2.1 (a) A *debit* entry records an account which gains value, or records an asset, or an expense.

(b) In the books of a business, the *credit* side of bank account records money paid out.

(c) In capital account, the initial capital contributed by the owner of the business is recorded on the *credit* side.

(d) Office equipment is an example of a *non-current (fixed)* asset.

(e) The purchase of a photocopier for use in the office is classed as *capital* expenditure.

(f) Repairs to a photocopier are classed as *revenue* expenditure.

2.2 ANDREW KING

(a)

Bank account

Dr			Cr		
20-4		£	20-4		£
1 Oct	Capital	7,500	4 Oct	Machinery	4,000
12 Oct	T Richards: loan	1,500	6 Oct	Office equipment	2,250
18 Oct	Commission received	200	11 Oct	Rent paid	400
			15 Oct	Wages	500
			20 Oct	Drawings	250
			25 Oct	Wages	450

(b)

Capital account

Dr			Cr		
20-4		£	20-4		£
			1 Oct	Bank	7,500

Machinery account

Dr			Cr		
20-4		£	20-4		£
4 Oct	Bank	4,000			

Office equipment account

Dr			Cr		
20-4		£	20-4		£
6 Oct	Bank	2,250			

Rent account

Dr			Cr		
20-4		£	20-4		£
11 Oct	Bank	400			

Tina Richards: loan account

Dr			Cr		
20-4		£	20-4		£
			12 Oct	Bank	1,500

Wages account

Dr			Cr		
20-4		£	20-4		£
15 Oct	Bank	500			
25 Oct	Bank	450			

Commission received account

Dr			Cr		
20-4		£	20-4		£
			18 Oct	Bank	200

Drawings account

Dr			Cr		
20-4		£	20-4		£
20 Oct	Bank	250			

2.3

Debit	*Credit*
purchases account	trade payables account

2.4

Debit	*Credit*
trade payables account	purchases returns account

2.5

Transaction	Account debited	Account credited
(a)	purchases	bank
(b)	bank	sales
(c)	purchases	Teme Traders
(d)	L Harris	sales
(e)	Teme Traders	purchases returns (returns out)
(f)	sales returns (returns in)	L Harris
(g)	bank	D Perkins: loan
(h)	cash	bank

2.6 PERSHORE PACKAGING

Purchases account

Dr					Cr
20-8		£	20-8		£
4 Jan	AB Supplies Limited	250			
20 Jan	Bank	225			

AB Supplies Limited

Dr					Cr
20-8		£	20-8		£
15 Jan	Bank	250	4 Jan	Purchases	250

Sales account

Dr					Cr
20-8		£	20-8		£
			5 Jan	Bank	195
			7 Jan	Cash	150
			18 Jan	L Lewis	145

Bank account

Dr					Cr
20-8		£	20-8		£
5 Jan	Sales	195	15 Jan	AB Supplies Limited	250
11 Jan	J Johnson: loan	1,000	20 Jan	Purchases	225
28 Jan	L Lewis	145	29 Jan	Mercia Office Supplies Ltd	160

Cash account

Dr					Cr
20-8		£	20-8		£
7 Jan	Sales	150	22 Jan	Wages	125

J Johnson: loan account

Dr					Cr
20-8		£	20-8		£
			11 Jan	Bank	1,000

L Lewis

Dr					Cr
20-8		£	20-8		£
18 Jan	Sales	145	28 Jan	Bank	145

Wages account

Dr					Cr
20-8		£	20-8		£
22 Jan	Cash	125			

Office equipment account

Dr					Cr
20-8		£	20-8		£
26 Jan	Mercia Office Supplies Ltd	160			

Mercia Office Supplies Limited

Dr					Cr
20-8		£	20-8		£
29 Jan	Bank	160	26 Jan	Office equipment	160

2.7 SONYA SMITH

Purchases account

Dr					Cr
20-6		£	20-6		£
2 Feb	G Lewis	200			
17 Feb	G Lewis	160			

Sales account

Dr					Cr
20-6		£	20-6		£
			4 Feb	L Jarvis	150
			8 Feb	G Patel	240

G Lewis

Dr					Cr
20-6		£	20-6		£
10 Feb	Bank	190	2 Feb	Purchases	200
10 Feb	Discount received	10	17 Feb	Purchases	160
24 Feb	Bank	152			
24 Feb	Discount received	8			
		360			360

L Jarvis

Dr					Cr
20-6		£	20-6		£
4 Feb	Sales	150	12 Feb	Bank	147
			12 Feb	Discount allowed	3
		150			150

G Patel

Dr					Cr
20-6		£	20-6		£
8 Feb	Sales	240	19 Feb	Bank	234
			19 Feb	Discount allowed	6
		240			240

Bank account

Dr					Cr
20-6		£	20-6		£
12 Feb	L Jarvis	147	10 Feb	G Lewis	190
19 Feb	G Patel	234	24 Feb	G Lewis	152

Discount received account

Dr					Cr
20-6		£	20-6		£
			10 Feb	G Lewis	10
			24 Feb	G Lewis	8

Discount allowed account

Dr					Cr
20-6		£	20-6		£
12 Feb	L Jarvis	3			
19 Feb	G Patel	6			

3 Chapter activities – answers
Balancing accounts and the trial balance

3.1 purchases

3.2 capital

3.3

TINA WONG
Trial balance as at 30 November 20-9

	Dr	Cr
	£	£
Bank		1,855
Capital (missing figure)		9,000
Cash	85	
Office equipment	2,500	
Purchases	2,419	
Purchases returns		102
Sales		4,164
Sales returns	354	
Trade payables (creditors)		1,082
Trade receivables (debtors)	2,115	
Vehicle	7,500	
Wages	1,230	
	16,203	16,203

3.4 (a)

LORNA FOX
Trial balance as at 31 March 20-1

	Dr	Cr
	£	£
Administration expenses	10,240	
Bank overdraft		1,050
Capital		155,440
Cash	150	
Drawings	9,450	
Interest paid	2,350	
Loan from bank		20,000
Machinery	40,000	
Premises	125,000	
Purchases	96,250	
Sales		146,390
Sales returns	8,500	
Telephone	3,020	
Trade payables (creditors)		10,545
Trade receivables (debtors)	10,390	
Travel expenses	1,045	
Value Added Tax		1,950
Wages	28,980	
	335,375	335,375

(b) See *Sole trader and partnership accounts: tutorial,* Chapter 2 and page 43. The explanation should be appropriate for someone who does not understand accounting.

3.5 (a) "You made an error of *principle* when you debited the cost of diesel fuel for the van to Vans Account."

(b) "There is a 'bad figure' on a purchases invoice – we have read it as £35 when it should be £55. It has gone through our accounts wrongly so we have an error of *original entry* to put right."

(c) "Who was in charge of that trainee last week? He has entered the payment for the electricity bill on the debit side of the bank and on the credit side of electricity – a *reversal* of *entries*"

(d) "I found this purchase invoice from last week in amongst the copy statements. As we haven't put it through the accounts we have an error of *omission*"

(e) "I've had the book-keeper from D Jones Limited on the 'phone concerning the statements of account that we sent out the other day. She says that there is a sales invoice charged that she knows nothing about. I wonder if we have done a *mispost* and it should be for T Jones' account?"

(f) "Although the trial balance balanced last week, I've since found an error of £100 in the calculation of the balance of sales account. We will need to check the other balances as I think we may have a *compensating* error."

3.6 (a) and (c) **MARK TANSALL**

Bank account

Dr			Cr		
20-4		£	20-4		£
1 Jan	Capital	10,000	4 Jan	Rent paid	500
11 Jan	Sales	2,400	5 Jan	Shop fittings	5,000
12 Jan	Sales	2,000	25 Jan	Purchases	3,000
20 Jan	Sales	1,500	27 Jan	Sales returns	280
22 Jan	Sales	2,250	31 Jan	Balance c/d	9,370
		18,150			18,150
1 Feb	Balance b/d	9,370	4 Feb	Rent paid	500
2 Feb	Sales	2,720	5 Feb	Shop fittings	1,550
10 Feb	Sales	3,995	12 Feb	Tech Software	7,500
22 Feb	Sales	1,930	19 Feb	Datasoft Ltd	5,000
24 Feb	Sales	2,145	28 Feb	Balance c/d	9,760
26 Feb	Sales	4,150			
		24,310			24,310
1 Mar	Balance b/d	9,760			

Capital account

Dr			Cr		
20-4		£	20-4		£
			1 Jan	Bank	10,000

Rent paid account

Dr			Cr		
20-4		£	20-4		£
4 Jan	Bank	500	28 Feb	Balance c/d	1,000
4 Feb	Bank	500			
		1,000			1,000
1 Mar	Balance b/d	1,000			

Shop fittings account

Dr			Cr		
20-4		£	20-4		£
5 Jan	Bank	5,000	28 Feb	Balance c/d	6,550
5 Feb	Bank	1,550			
		6,550			6,550
1 Mar	Balance b/d	6,550			

Dr		**Purchases account**			Cr
20-4		£	20-4		£
7 Jan	Tech Software	7,500	31 Jan	Balance c/d	15,500
16 Jan	Datasoft Ltd	5,000			
25 Jan	Bank	3,000			
		15,500			15,500
1 Feb	Balance b/d	15,500	28 Feb	Balance c/d	22,130
15 Feb	Tech Software	4,510			
25 Feb	Associated Software	2,120			
		22,130			22,130
1 Mar	Balance b/d	22,130			

Dr		**Tech Software**			Cr
20-4		£	20-4		£
12 Feb	Bank	7,500	7 Jan	Purchases	7,500
28 Feb	Balance c/d	4,510	15 Feb	Purchases	4,510
		12,010			12,010
			1 Mar	Balance b/d	4,510

Dr		**Sales account**			Cr
20-4		£	20-4		£
31 Jan	Balance c/d	10,645	11 Jan	Bank	2,400
			12 Jan	Bank	2,000
			20 Jan	Bank	1,500
			22 Jan	Bank	2,250
			29 Jan	Teme College	2,495
		10,645			10,645
28 Feb	Balance c/d	25,585	1 Feb	Balance b/d	10,645
			2 Feb	Bank	2,720
			10 Feb	Bank	3,995
			22 Feb	Bank	1,930
			24 Feb	Bank	2,145
			26 Feb	Bank	4,150
		25,585			25,585
			1 Mar	Balance b/d	25,585

Dr		Datasoft Limited			Cr
20-4		£	20-4		£
19 Feb	Bank	5,000	16 Jan	Purchases	5,000

Dr		Sales returns account			Cr
20-4		£	20-4		£
27 Jan	Bank	280	28 Feb	Balance c/d	425
23 Feb	Teme College	145			
		425			425
1 Mar	Balance b/d	425			

Dr		Teme College			Cr
20-4		£	20-4		£
29 Jan	Sales	2,495	23 Feb	Sales returns	145
			28 Feb	Balance c/d	2,350
		2,495			2,495
1 Mar	Balance b/d	2,350			

Dr		Associated Software			Cr
20-4		£	20-4		£
			25 Feb	Purchases	2,120

(b) **Trial balance as at 31 January 20-4**

	Dr	Cr
	£	£
Bank	9,370	
Capital		10,000
Rent paid	500	
Shop fittings	5,000	
Purchases	15,500	
Tech Software		7,500
Sales		10,645
Datasoft Limited		5,000
Sales returns	280	
Teme College	2,495	
	33,145	33,145

(d) **Trial balance as at 28 February 20-4**

	Dr	Cr
	£	£
Bank	9,760	
Capital		10,000
Rent paid	1,000	
Shop fittings	6,550	
Purchases	22,130	
Tech Software		4,510
Sales		25,585
Sales returns	425	
Teme College	2,350	
Associated Software		2,120
	42,215	42,215

4 Chapter activities – answers

Financial statements – the extended trial balance

4.1 cash

4.2 sales revenue

4.3 EXTENDED TRIAL BALANCE — MATT SMITH — 31 DECEMBER 20-3

Account name	Ledger balances		Adjustments		Income statement		Statement of financial position	
	Dr £	*Cr* £	*Dr* £	*Cr* £	*Dr* £	*Cr* £	*Dr* £	*Cr* £
Opening inventory	14,350				14,350			
Purchases	114,472				114,472			
Sales revenue		259,688				259,688		
Rent and rates	13,718				13,718			
Heating and lighting	12,540				12,540			
Wages and salaries	42,614				42,614			
Vehicle expenses	5,817				5,817			
Advertising	6,341				6,341			
Premises at cost	75,000						75,000	
Office equipment at cost	33,000						33,000	
Vehicles at cost	21,500						21,500	
Sales ledger control	23,854						23,854	
Bank	1,235						1,235	
Cash	125						125	
Capital		62,500						62,500
Drawings	12,358						12,358	
Loan from bank		35,000						35,000
Purchases ledger control		14,258						14,258
Value Added Tax		5,478						5,478
Closing inventory: income statement		16,280				16,280		
Closing inventory: statement of financial position	16,280						16,280	
Profit/loss for the year					66,116			66,116
	393,204	393,204			275,968	275,968	183,352	183,352

4.4 EXTENDED TRIAL BALANCE — **CLARE LEWIS** — **31 DECEMBER 20-4**

Account name	Ledger balances		Adjustments		Income statement		Statement of financial position	
	Dr £	*Cr* £	*Dr* £	*Cr* £	*Dr* £	*Cr* £	*Dr* £	*Cr* £
Sales ledger control	18,600						18,600	
Purchases ledger control		11,480						11,480
Value Added Tax		1,870						1,870
Bank		4,610						4,610
Capital		25,250						25,250
Sales revenue		144,810				144,810		
Purchases	96,318				96,318			
Opening inventory	16,010				16,010			
Salaries	18,465				18,465			
Heating and lighting	1,820				1,820			
Rent and rates	5,647				5,647			
Vehicles at cost	9,820						9,820	
Office equipment at cost	5,500						5,500	
Sundry expenses	845				845			
Vehicle expenses	1,684				1,684			
Drawings	13,311						13,311	
Closing inventory: income statement		13,735				13,735		
Closing inventory: statement of financial position	13,735						13,735	
Profit/loss for the year					17,756			17,756
	201,755	201,755			158,545	158,545	60,966	60,966

5 Chapter activities – answers Accruals and prepayments

5.1 a liability and an expense accrued

5.2 vehicle expenses prepaid

5.3 (a) **Selling expenses**

	£		£
Bank	12,700	Balance b/d	400
		Income statement	11,750
		Balance c/d	550
	12,700		12,700

(b) **Vehicle expenses**

		£			£
20-1 1 Apr	Balance b/d	150	20-2 31 Mar	Income statement	7,630
20-2 31 Mar	Bank	7,200			
20-2 31 Mar	Balance c/d	280			
		7,630			7,630

(c)

Account	**£**	**£ Dr**	**£ Cr**
Accruals			280
Capital	45,000		45,000
Discount allowed	470	470	
Drawings	12,500	12,500	
Interest paid	380	380	
Office equipment at cost	24,500	24,500	
Prepayments		550	
Purchases returns	2,740		2,740

5.4 EXTENDED TRIAL BALANCE — **CINDY HAYWARD** — **30 JUNE 20-4**

Account name	Ledger balances		Adjustments		Income statement		Statement of financial position	
	Dr £	Cr £	Dr £	Cr £	Dr £	Cr £	Dr £	Cr £
Capital		90,932						90,932
Drawings	10,000		200				10,200	
Purchases	148,500			200	148,300			
Sales revenue		210,900				210,900		
Repairs to buildings	848				848			
Vehicles at cost	15,000						15,000	
Vehicle expenses	1,540		85		1,625			
Land and buildings at cost	185,000						185,000	
Loan from bank		110,000						110,000
Bank	540						540	
Shop fittings at cost	12,560						12,560	
Wages	30,280		560		30,840			
Discount allowed	135				135			
Discount received		1,319				1,319		
Rates and insurance	2,690			255	2,435			
Sales ledger control	3,175						3,175	
Purchases ledger control		8,295						8,295
Heating and lighting	3,164				3,164			
General expenses	4,680				4,680			
Sales returns	855				855			
Purchases returns		1,221				1,221		
Opening inventory	6,210				6,210			
Value Added Tax		2,510						2,510
Closing inventory: income statement		7,515				7,515		
Closing inventory: statement of financial position	7,515						7,515	
Accruals				645				645
Prepayments			255				255	
Profit/loss for the year					21,863			21,863
	432,692	432,692	1,100	1,100	220,955	220,955	234,245	234,245

6 Chapter activities – answers
Depreciation of non-current assets

6.1 £6,860

6.2 30%

6.3 loss on disposal of £30

6.4

	Debit	*Credit*
	disposals account	income statement

6.5 (a)

year 1	£1,600
year 2	£1,280
total	£2,880

(b) **Machine at cost**

Balance b/d	£8,000	Disposals	£8,000
	£8,000		£8,000

Machine: disposals

Machine at cost	£8,000	Machine: accumulated depreciation	£2,880
		Bank	£4,800
		Income statement	£320
	£8,000		£8,000

Bank

Machine disposals	£4,800	Balance c/d	£5,760
Value Added Tax	£960		
	£5,760		£5,760

(c)

profit	
loss	✔

6.6 EXTENDED TRIAL BALANCE **WINTERGREEN SUPPLIES** **31 DECEMBER 20-6**

Account name	Ledger balances		Adjustments		Income statement		Statement of financial position	
	Dr £	*Cr* £	*Dr* £	*Cr* £	*Dr* £	*Cr* £	*Dr* £	*Cr* £
Premises at cost	120,000						120,000	
Premises: accumulated depreciation		7,200		2,400				9,600
Bank loan		52,800						52,800
Capital		70,000						70,000
Sales ledger control	11,900						11,900	
Purchases ledger control		11,500						11,500
Drawings	6,750						6,750	
Cash	150						150	
Opening inventory	4,200				4,200			
Office equipment at cost	5,000						5,000	
Office equipment: accumulated depreciation		1,000		1,000				2,000
Vehicles at cost	10,000						10,000	
Vehicles: accumulated depreciation		2,000		2,000				4,000
Bank		750						750
Sales revenue		194,850				194,850		
Purchases	154,000				154,000			
Wages	20,500			560	19,940			
Sundry expenses	9,500		500		10,000			
Value Added Tax		1,750						1,750
Disposal of non-current asset		150				150		
Closing inventory: income statement		5,200				5,200		
Closing inventory: statement of financial position	5,200						5,200	
Accruals				500				500
Prepayments			560				560	
Depreciation charge			5,400		5,400			
Profit/loss for the year					6,660			6,660
	347,200	347,200	6,460	6,460	200,200	200,200	159,560	159,560

7 Chapter activities – answers
Irrecoverable debts and allowance for doubtful debts

7.1

Debit	*Credit*
irrecoverable debts account	T Neal's account

Tutorial note: where control accounts – see Chapter 10 of the *Tutorial* – are in use, the credit entry will be to sales ledger control account.

7.2 decrease profit for the year

7.3 £2,270

7.4

Year	Income statement			Statement of financial position	
	Dr *irrecoverable debts* £	Dr *allowance for doubtful debts: adjustment* £	Cr *allowance for doubtful debts: adjustment* £	Dr *sales ledger control (receivables)* £	Cr *allowance for doubtful debts* £
20-5	1,800	2,585	–	103,400	2,585
20-6	2,400	245	–	113,200	2,830
20-7	1,400	–	110	108,800	2,720

7.5 (a) **Irrecoverable debts**

	£		£
Sales ledger control (Craven Traders)	75	Income statement	240
Sales ledger control (Harris and Co)	110		
Sales ledger control (P Mahon)	55		
	240		240

(b) **Allowance for doubtful debts**

		£			£
20-6 31 Dec	Allowance for doubtful debts: adjustment	50	20-6 01 Jan	Balance b/d	300
20-6 31 Dec	Balance c/d	250			
		300			300

(c)

Account	**Ledger balances**		**Adjustments**	
	Dr £	**Cr £**	**Dr £**	**Cr £**
Allowance for doubtful debts		300	50	
Allowance for doubtful debts: adjustment				50
Irrecoverable debts			240	
Purchases ledger control		8,960		
Sales ledger control	12,740			240
Vehicles at cost	20,000			
Vehicles: accumulated depreciation		11,200		
Wages	22,850			

7.6 EXTENDED TRIAL BALANCE — JANE JONES — 31 DECEMBER 20-5

Account name	Ledger balances		Adjustments		Income statement		Statement of financial position	
	Dr £	*Cr* £	*Dr* £	*Cr* £	*Dr* £	*Cr* £	*Dr* £	*Cr* £
Sales ledger control	37,200			2,200			35,000	
Purchases ledger control		30,640						30,640
Value Added Tax		4,280						4,280
Bank	14,640						14,640	
Capital		50,500						50,500
Sales revenue		289,620				289,620		
Purchases	182,636				182,636			
Opening inventory	32,020				32,020			
Wages and salaries	36,930				36,930			
Heat and light	3,640				3,640			
Rent and rates	11,294			2,190	9,104			
Vehicles at cost	20,000						20,000	
Vehicles: accumulated depreciation		4,000		3,200				7,200
Machinery at cost	10,000						10,000	
Machinery: accumulated depreciation		1,000		900				1,900
Sundry expenses	1,690		270		1,960			
Vehicle expenses	3,368				3,368			
Drawings	26,622						26,622	
Closing inventory: income statement		34,000				34,000		
Closing inventory: statement of financial position	34,000						34,000	
Accruals				270				270
Prepayments			2,190				2,190	
Depreciation charge			4,100		4,100			
Irrecoverable debts			2,200		2,200			
Allowance for doubtful debts				1,750				1,750
Allowance for doubtful debts: adjustment			1,750		1,750			
Profit/loss for the year					45,912			45,912
	414,040	414,040	10,510	10,510	323,620	323,620	142,452	142,452

8 Chapter activities – answers The rules of accounting

8.1 (a) The accounting concept of materiality means that some items in accounts are of such a low monetary value that it is not worthwhile recording them separately, ie they are not 'material'.

(b)
- Small expense items do not justify their own separate expense account; instead they are grouped together in a sundry expenses account.
- End-of-year unused office stationery is often not valued for the purpose of financial statements, because the amount is not material and does not justify the time and effort involved.
- Low-cost non-current assets are often charged as an expense in the income statement, instead of being classed as capital expenditure.

8.2 (a) increase profit for the year.

Tutorial notes:

- With falling prices,
  - FIFO gives a lower closing inventory valuation (because the closing inventory consists of the most recently purchased items)
  - LIFO gives a higher closing inventory valuation (because the closing inventory consists of the oldest purchased items)
- In this year's income statement, cost of sales will be
  - higher under FIFO, giving a lower profit
  - lower under LIFO, giving a higher profit
- This year's closing inventory valuation will affect next year's profit – over the life of a business, total profit is the same whichever method of inventory valuation is used.

(b) consistency

8.3 (a) IAS 2 *Inventories* states that inventories are to be valued at *the lower of cost and net realisable value.*

(b)

	FIFO ✔	LIFO ✔
£54		
£61	✔	
£60		
£48		✔
£40		
£135		

Tutorial notes:

The closing inventory is:

	units bought (20 + 10 + 10)	=	40
less	units sold (8 + 16)	=	24
equals	closing inventory	=	16

(a) FIFO

6 units at £3.50	=	£21.00
10 units at £4.00	=	£40.00
16 units	=	£61.00

(b) LIFO

16 units at £3.00	=	£48.00

8.4 (a) Sales revenue for the half year:

		£
• product Y, 220 units at £10.00 each	=	2,200.00
• product Z, 340 units at £16.00 each	=	5,440.00
• total sales	=	7,640.00

(b) Product Y:

		£
20 units at £4.20 per unit	=	84.00
100 units at £3.80 per unit	=	380.00
80 units at £4.50 per unit	=	360.00
200 units	=	824.00

Product Z:

		£
60 units at £10.50 per unit	=	630.00
140 units at £10.00 per unit	=	1,400.00
200 units	=	2,030.00

(c)

		£	
• Product Y	=	824.00	(cost price)
• Product Z	=	1,950.00	(net realisable value)
		2,774.00	

(d) Purchases

		£
• product Y	=	1,728.00
• product Z	=	5,400.00
		7,128.00
Less closing inventory	=	2,774.00
Cost of sales		4,354.00

8.5 quarterly electricity bill

8.6 cost of materials used to extend the premises

8.7 debited to the income statement

8.8

	capital expenditure ✔	revenue expenditure ✔
(a) purchase of vehicles	✔	
(b) depreciation of vehicles		✔
(c) rent paid on premises		✔
(d) wages and salaries		✔
(e) legal fees relating to the purchase of property	✔	
(f) redecoration of office		✔
(g) installation of air-conditioning in office	✔	
(h) wages of own employees used to build extension to the office	✔	
(i) installation and setting up of a new machine	✔	

9 Chapter activities – answers Accounting for capital transactions

9.1 goodwill

9.2 at the end of the hire purchase period, ownership of the computer will be transferred from the finance company to Eveshore Enterprises

9.3 Depreciation calculations:

	20-2	20-3	20-4	TOTAL
	£	£	£	£
Van 1	4,000	3,000	–	7,000
Van 2	4,000	3,000	2,250	9,250
Van 3	–	–	4,500	4,500
Van 4	–	–	4,500	4,500
TOTAL	8,000	6,000	11,250	25,250

Vehicles at cost account

Dr					Cr
20-2		£	20-2		£
01 Jan	Bank	16,000	31 Dec	Balance c/d	32,000
01 Jan	Bank	16,000			
		32,000			32,000
20-3			20-3		
01 Jan	Balance b/d	32,000	31 Dec	Balance c/d	32,000
20-4			20-4		
01 Jan	Balance b/d	32,000	20 Mar	Disposals	16,000
01 Jan	Bank	18,000	31 Dec	Balance c/d	52,000
01 Jan	Bank	18,000			
		68,000			68,000
20-5			20-5		
01 Jan	Balance b/d	52,000			

Depreciation charge account

Dr					Cr
20-2		£	20-2		£
31 Dec	Vehicles: accumulated depreciation	8,000	31 Dec	Income statement	8,000
20-3			20-3		
31 Dec	Vehicles: accumulated depreciation	6,000	31 Dec	Income statement	6,000
20-4			20-4		
31 Dec	Vehicles: accumulated depreciation	11,250	31 Dec	Income statement	11,250

Vehicles: accumulated depreciation account

Dr		£			Cr £
20-2		£	20-2		£
31 Dec	Balance c/d	8,000	31 Dec	Depreciation charge	8,000
20-3			20-3		
31 Dec	Balance c/d	14,000	01 Jan	Balance b/d	8,000
			31 Dec	Depreciation charge	6,000
		14,000			14,000
20-4			20-4		
20 Mar	Disposals	7,000	01 Jan	Balance b/d	14,000
31 Dec	Balance c/d	18,250	31 Dec	Depreciation charge	11,250
		25,250			25,250
20-5			20-5		
			01 Jan	Balance b/d	18,250

Vehicle disposals account

Dr					Cr
20-4		£	20-4		£
20 Mar	Vehicles	16,000	20 Mar	Vehicles: accumulated depreciation	7,000
			20 Mar	Bank	8,000
			20 Mar	Income statement (loss on disposal)	1,000
		16,000			16,000

9.4 Jane should consider:

- hire purchase
- a finance lease

Hire purchase

- An agreement with a finance company which will enable Speedprint (the hirer) to have the use of the new printing machine on payment of a deposit.
- The finance company owns the printing machine and Speedprint will make regular instalment payments – monthly, quarterly or half-yearly – which will pay back the cost plus interest over a set period.
- At the end of the hire purchase period, ownership of the printing machine will pass from the finance company to Speedprint.

Finance lease

- An agreement whereby Speedprint (the lessee) has the use of the printing machine, which is owned by a finance company (the lessor).
- Speedprint will make regular rental payments to the lessor over the period of the lease, which might be up to seven years.
- There is normally no provision in a finance lease for legal ownership of the leased asset to pass to the lessee at the end of the lease.

9.5

NON-CURRENT ASSET REGISTER							
Description/serial no	**Acquisition date**	**Cost £**	**Depreciation £**	**Carrying amount £**	**Funding method**	**Disposal proceeds £**	**Disposal date**
Machinery							
Moulding machine	12/08/-3	10,000.00			Cash		
Year end 31/03/-4			2,000.00	8,000.00			
Year end 31/03/-5			2,000.00	6,000.00			
Year end 31/03/-6			2,000.00	4,000.00			
Pressing machine	17/06/-5	2,660.00			Cash		
Year end 31/03/-6			532.00	2,128.00			
Vehicles							
AB03 TPJ	11/06/-3	16,400.00			Cash		
Year end 31/03/-4			4,100.00	12,300.00			
Year end 31/03/-5			3,075.00	9,225.00			
Year end 31/03/-6			–	–		8,000.00	14/02/-6
AB54 PZE	01/01/-5	15,200.00			Part-exchange		
Year end 31/03/-5			3,800.00	11,400.00			
Year end 31/03/-6			2,850.00	8,550.00			

Tutorial notes:

- installation of the pressing machine is capitalised
- the service contract is revenue expenditure

10 Chapter activities – answers
Control accounts

10.1

Error	Difference ✔	No difference ✔
Sales returns day book was undercast by £100.	✔	
A credit note for £75 was credited to the account of Martley Traders instead of Martley Manufacturing – both are sales ledger accounts.		✔
The sales ledger account of C Fernandez, £125, has been written off as irrecoverable, but no entry has been made in sales ledger control account.	✔	
A set-off entry for £45 has been incorrectly recorded as £54 in the sales ledger control account and in the sales ledger account.		✔

10.2

		£
Total of list of purchases ledger balances		55,946
Adjustment for (a)	add	18
Adjustment for (b)	subtract	200
Adjustment for (c)	subtract	141
Adjustment for (d)	subtract	225
Revised total to agree with purchases ledger control account		55,398

10.3

Adjustment number	Amount £	Debit ✓	Credit ✓
1	120		✓
3	100		✓
4	95		✓

10.4

Adjustment number	Amount £	Debit ✓	Credit ✓
1	500		✓
2	190	✓	
4	280	✓	

10.5

Adjustment number	Amount £	Debit ✓	Credit ✓
2	360		✓
3	90		✓
4	120		✓

11 Chapter activities – answers
The journal and correction of errors

11.1 bank payment to a trade payable

11.2

Debit		*Credit*	
Stationery	£25	Office equipment	£25

11.3

Debit		*Credit*	
Suspense	£36	Vehicle repairs	£36
Vehicle repairs	£63	Suspense	£63

11.4

Adjustment	**Profit increases** ✔	**Profit decreases** ✔
sales account has been overcast		✔
closing inventory has been undervalued	✔	
telephone expenses account has been undercast		✔
discount received has been omitted	✔	
depreciation charge for vehicles has been omitted		✔
a trade receivable account is written off as irrecoverable		✔
a reduction in the allowance for doubtful debts is made	✔	

11.5 (a) Journal

	Dr £	Cr £
Irrecoverable debts	300	
Sales ledger control		300

(b) Journal

	Dr £	Cr £
Office equipment	4,000	
Suspense		4,000

(c) Journal

	Dr £	Cr £
Closing inventory – statement of financial position	*18,140	
Closing inventory – income statement		*18,140

* lower of cost and net realisable value: £18,380 – £240

(d) Journal

	Dr £	Cr £
VAT	920	
Suspense		920
VAT	920	
Suspense		920

11.6 Extended trial balance

Ledger account	Ledger balances		Adjustments		Income statement		Statement of financial position	
	£ Dr	£ Cr	£ Dr	£ Cr	£ Dr	£ Cr	£ Dr	£ Cr
Allowance for doubtful debts		1,200	100					1,100
Allowance for doubtful debts adjustment				100		100		
Bank	15,300						15,300	
Capital		30,000						30,000
Closing inventory			25,230	25,230		25,230	25,230	
Depreciation charge			2,500		2,500			
Office equipment at cost	20,000						20,000	
Office equipment: accumulated depreciation		8,500		2,500				11,000
Office expenses	12,700		500		13,200			
Opening inventory	22,680				22,680			
Payroll expenses	25,920			350	25,570			
Purchases	85,500		400		85,900			
Purchases ledger control		25,270						25,270
Rent and rates	5,400			250	5,150			
Sales		151,200				151,200		
Sales ledger control	30,380						30,380	
Suspense	300		600	900				
VAT		2,010						2,010
Profit/loss for the year					21,530			21,530
	218,180	218,180	29,330	29,330	176,530	176,530	90,910	90,910

Tutorial note: the debit balance on suspense account is cleared by the debit adjustment of £600 (£350 and £250), and the credit adjustment of £900 (£500 and £400).

Accounts preparation I

Practice assessment 1

Time allowance: 2 hours

- Each task of the Assessment is to be answered separately.
- The rate of Value Added Tax used is 20%.

Section 1: Accounting for non-current (fixed) assets

Task 1.1

This task is about recording information for non-current assets for a business known as Toynton Trading. Toynton Trading is registered for VAT.

The following is a purchase invoice received by Toynton Trading:

To: Toynton Trading Toynton House The High Road Toynton TN2 7RD	**Invoice 2945** Laptop Supplies plc Unit 10, Fairway Estate Wyvern WV1 2XR		**Date:** 26 March 20X0
PHX laptop computer	Serial no 415762XZ	1	740.00
Next-day delivery		1	10.00
Laptop carry bag		1	20.00
VAT @ 20%			154.00
Total			924.00
Settlement terms: strictly 30 days net			

The following information relates to the sale of a car:

Registration number	PT07 PZV
Date of sale	14 March 20X0
Selling price	£7,500.00

- Toynton Trading has a policy of capitalising expenditure over £500.
- Vehicles are depreciated at 25% on a reducing balance basis.
- Computer equipment is depreciated at 30% on a straight-line basis assuming no residual value.
- Non-current assets are depreciated in the year of acquisition but not in the year of disposal.

Record the following information in the non-current asset register on the next page:

(a) Any acquisitions of non-current assets during the year ended 31 March 20X0

(b) Any disposals of non-current assets during the year ended 31 March 20X0

(c) Depreciation for the year ended 31 March 20X0

NON-CURRENT ASSET REGISTER							
Description/serial no	**Acquisition date**	**Cost £**	**Depreciation £**	**Carrying amount £**	**Funding method**	**Disposal proceeds £**	**Disposal date**
Computer equipment							
PHX Laser printer	15/12/X7	1,200.00			Cash		
Year end 31/03/X8			360.00	840.00			
Year end 31/03/X9			360.00	480.00			
Year end 31/03/X0							
Year end 31/03/X0							
Vehicles							
PT07 PZV	20/05/X7	16,000.00			Cash		
Year end 31/03/X8			4,000.00	12,000.00			
Year end 31/03/X9			3,000.00	9,000.00			
Year end 31/03/X0							
PT58 ZPE	19/11/X8	14,400.00			Part-exchange		
Year end 31/03/X9			3,600.00	10,800.00			
Year end 31/03/X0							

Task 1.2

This task is about recording non-current asset information in the general ledger and other non-current asset matters.

- You are working on the accounts of a business that is registered for VAT.
- A new machine has been acquired. VAT can be reclaimed on this machine.
- The cost excluding VAT was £6,000; this was paid from the bank.
- The residual value is expected to be £2,000 excluding VAT.
- The depreciation policy for machines is that they are depreciated on a straight line basis over five years.
- Depreciation has already been entered into the accounts for the existing machines.

Make entries to account for:

(a) The purchase of the new machine

(b) The depreciation on the new machine

On each account, show clearly the balance carried down or transferred to the income statement.

Machinery at cost

Balance b/d	£25,000		

Machinery: accumulated depreciation

		Balance b/d	£8,000

Machinery: depreciation charge

Balance b/d	£1,000		

(c) The business keeps a non-current asset register of the machinery owned by the business. Which ONE of the following statements regarding a non-current asset register is TRUE?

	✔
It shows the carrying amount of each machine	
It proves legal ownership of each machine	
It shows how much each machine will be sold for when it is disposed	
It shows when it is time to replace each machine	

Section 2: Extending the trial balance using accounting adjustments

Task 2.1

This task is about accounting for accruals and prepayments and preparing a trial balance.

You are working on the accounts of a business for the year ended 31 March 20X1. In this task you can ignore VAT.

You have the following information:

Balances as at:	**1 April 20X0** **£**
Accrual for vehicle expenses	300
Prepayment for selling expenses	450

The bank summary for the year shows payments for vehicle expenses of £5,540. Included in this figure is £780 for the quarter ended 31 May 20X1.

(a) **Prepare the vehicle expenses account for the year ended 31 March 20X1 and close it off by showing the transfer to the income statement.**

Vehicle expenses

	£		£

The bank summary for the year shows payments for selling expenses of £11,650. In April 20X1, £290 was paid for selling expenses incurred in March 20X1.

(b) Prepare the selling expenses account for the year ended 31 March 20X1 and close it off by showing the transfer to the income statement. Include dates.

Selling expenses

		£			£

You have the following extract of balances from the general ledger.

(c) Using your answers to (a) and (b), and the figures given below, enter amounts in the appropriate debit or credit column for the accounts shown. Do NOT enter zeros in unused column cells.

Extract from trial balance as at 31 March 20X1

Account	**£**	**£ Dr**	**£ Cr**
Accruals			
Capital	40,000		
Discount allowed	470		
Drawings	18,500		
Interest received	350		
Office equipment at cost	15,000		
Office equipment: accumulated depreciation	6,500		
Prepayments			

Task 2.2

This task is about recording journal entries.

You are working on the financial statements of a business with a year end of 31 March. A trial balance has been drawn up and a suspense account opened with a debit balance of £1,080. You now need to make some corrections and adjustments for the year ended 31 March 20X1.

Record the journal entries needed in the general ledger to deal with the items below. You should:

- remove any incorrect entries, where appropriate
- post the correct entries

You do not need to give narratives.

Do NOT enter zeros into unused column cells.

(a) Entries need to be made for an irrecoverable debt of £150. Ignore VAT.

Journal

	Dr £	Cr £

(b) A payment for rent of £600 has been made from the bank. The correct entry was made to the bank account, but no other entries were made.

Journal

	Dr £	Cr £

(c) No entries have been made for closing inventory for the year end 31 March 20X1. Closing inventory has been valued at cost at £18,300. Included in this figure are some items costing £2,020 that will be sold for £1,500.

Journal

	Dr £	Cr £

(d) The figures from the columns of the sales returns day book for 31 March have been totalled correctly as follows:

Sales returns column	£1,200
VAT column	£240
Total column	£1,440

The amounts have been posted as follows:

Dr Sales returns	£1,200
Cr VAT	£240
Cr Sales ledger control	£1,440

Journal

	Dr £	Cr £

Task 2.3

This task is about completing an extended balance.

You have the following extended trial balance. The adjustments have already been correctly entered.

Extend the figures into the income statement and statement of financial position.

Do NOT enter zeros into unused column cells.

Make the columns balance by entering figures in the correct places.

Extended trial balance

Ledger account	Ledger balances		Adjustments		Income statement		Statement of financial position	
	£ Dr	£ Cr	£ Dr	£ Cr	£ Dr	£ Cr	£ Dr	£ Cr
Allowance for doubtful debts		2,100	250					
Allowance for doubtful debts adjustment				250				
Bank	3,700			200				
Capital		40,000						
Closing inventory			21,300	21,300				
Depreciation charge			2,750					
Machinery at cost	25,000							
Machinery: accumulated depreciation		11,500		2,750				
Office expenses	7,350			300				
Opening inventory	19,100							
Payroll expenses	16,850		500					
Purchases	76,200							
Purchases ledger control		11,400						
Sales		118,200	450					
Sales ledger control	30,950							
Selling expenses	5,750							
Suspense	450		500	950				
VAT		2,150						
Profit/loss for the year								
	185,350	185,350	25,750	25,750				

Task 2.4

This task is about preparing reconciliations.

The sales ledger has been compared with sales ledger control account and the following differences identified:

1. The total column of sales returns day book has been overcast (overadded) by £100.
2. Settlement (cash) discount allowed of £300 has been entered in the sales ledger accounts but has been omitted from sales ledger control account.
3. A credit sale of £550 has been debited to the sales ledger account of H Gaskin Ltd instead of the sales ledger account of Haskins Ltd.
4. The account of Whittle Ltd, £150, has been written off as irrecoverable in sales ledger, but has not been recorded in sales ledger control account.

The total of the account balances in sales ledger is £22,170 debit and the balance of sales ledger control account is £22,520 debit.

Use the following table to show the three adjustments you need to make to sales ledger control account.

Adjustment number	Amount £	Debit ✓	Credit ✓

Task 2.5

This task is to test your knowledge. Choose ONE answer from each part.

(a) A business should not, without good reason, change its method of depreciation. This follows the accounting principle (concept) of:

	✔
going concern	
accruals	
prudence	
consistency	

(b) Day books are kept:

	✔
instead of double-entry accounts	
to gather and summarise accounting information for the double-entry system	
to show how much is owed to suppliers and by customers	
to show the assets and liabilities of the business	

Accounts preparation I

Practice assessment 2

Time allowance: 2 hours

- This Assessment is based on a sample assessment provided by the AAT and is reproduced here with their kind permission.
- Each task of the Assessment is to be answered separately.
- The rate of Value Added Tax used is 20%.

Section 1: Accounting for non-current (fixed) assets

Task 1.1

This task is about recording information for fixed assets for a business known as Amber Trading. Amber Trading is registered for VAT.

The following is a purchase invoice received by Amber Trading:

To: **Amber Trading** Unit 6, East End Trading Estate Southgrove HP14 6PW	**Invoice 634** Computer Supplies plc 12 Hanger Lane Bedgrove HP12 1AA		**Date:** 28 March X0
HP colour laser printer	Serial number 65438LKR	1	750.00
Delivery		1	25.00
Printer cartridges @ £20.00 each		2	40.00
VAT @20%			163.00
Total			978.00
Settlement terms: strictly 30 days net			

The following information relates to the sale of a vehicle:

Registration number	AB 08 DRF
Date of sale	15 March X0
Selling price excluding VAT	£5500.00

- Amber Trading has a policy of capitalising expenditure over £500.
- Vehicles are depreciated at 25% on a reducing balance basis.
- Computer equipment is depreciated at 30% on a straight-line basis assuming no residual value.
- Fixed assets are depreciated in the year of acquisition but not in the year of disposal.

Record the following information in the fixed assets (non-current assets) register on the following page:

(a) Any acquisitions of fixed assets during the year ended 31 March X0

(b) Any disposals of fixed assets during the year ended 31 March X0

(c) Depreciation for the year ended 31 March X0

Fixed assets register

Description	*Acquisition date*	*Cost £*	*Depreciation £*	*Net book value £*	*Funding method*	*Disposal proceeds*	*Disposal date*
Computer equipment							
Server main office	30/09/X7	2,800.00			Cash		
Year end 31/03/X8			840.00	1,960.00			
Year end 31/03/X9			840.00	1,120.00			
Year end 31/03/X0							
Year end 31/03/X0							
Motor Vehicles							
AB08 DRF	01/04/X7	12,000.00			Cash		
Year end 31/03/X8			3,000.00	9,000.00			
Year end 31/03/X9			2,250.00	6,750.00			
Year end 31/03/X0							
AB07 FRP	31/01/X9	9,600.00			Part-exchange		
Year end 31/03/X9			2,400.00	7,200.00			
Year end 31/03/X0							

Task 1.2

This task is about recording fixed asset (non-current asset) information in the nominal (general, main) ledger and other fixed asset matters.

- You are working on the accounts of a partnership business that is registered for VAT.
- A new vehicle has been acquired. VAT can be reclaimed on this vehicle.
- The cost excluding VAT was £4,000; this was paid from the bank.
- The residual value is expected to be £1,500 excluding VAT.
- The depreciation policy for vehicles is 25% per annum on a straight line basis.
- Depreciation has already been entered into the accounts for the existing vehicles.

Make entries to account for:

(a) The purchase of the new vehicle

(b) The depreciation on the new vehicle

On each account, show clearly the balance carried down or transferred to the profit and loss account.

Vehicles at cost

Balance b/d	10,000		

Vehicles accumulated depreciation

		Balance b/d	3,000

Depreciation charge

Balance b/d	1,000		

(c) The business needs to develop a policy for authorisation of new vehicles purchases. Choose the ONE most suitable policy.

New vehicle purchases should be authorised by:	✓
(a) A partner of the business	
(b) The driver of the vehicle	
(c) A bank signatory	
(d) An accounting technician	

Section 2 – Extending the trial balance using accounting adjustments

Task 2.1

This task is about accounting for accruals and prepayments and preparing a trial balance.

You are working on the final accounts of a business for the year ended 31 March 20X1. In this task, you can ignore VAT.

You have the following information:

Balances as at:	1 April 20X0 £
Accrual for administration expenses	790
Prepayment for selling expenses	375

The bank summary for the year shows payments for administration expenses of £6,190. Included in this figure is £1,800 for the quarter ended 31 May 20X1.

(a) Prepare the administration expenses account for the year ended 31 March 20X1 and close it off by showing the transfer to the profit and loss account.

Administration expenses

	£		£

The bank summary for the year shows payments for selling expenses of £7,900. In April 20X1, £825 was paid for selling expenses incurred in March 20X1.

(b) Prepare the selling expenses account for the year ended 31 March 20X1 and close it off by showing the transfer to the profit and loss account. Include dates.

Selling expenses

		£			£

You have the following extract of balances from the nominal (main, general) ledger.

(c) Using your answers to (a) and (b), and the figures given below, enter amounts in the appropriate column for the accounts shown. Do NOT enter zeros in unused column cells.

Extract from trial balance as at 31 March 20X1.

Account	*£*	*£ Dr*	*£ Cr*
Accruals			
Capital	6,000		
Depreciation charge	850		
Drawings	11,000		
Interest received	70		
Machinery at cost	5,600		
Machinery accumulated depreciation	4,200		
Prepayments			

Task 2.2*

This task is about recording journal entries.

You are working on the final accounts of a business with a year-end of 31 March. A trial balance has been drawn up and a suspense account opened with a debit balance of £1,700. You now need to make some corrections and adjustments for the year ended 31 March 20X1.

Record the journal entries needed in the nominal (main, general) ledger to deal with the items below.

You should:

- Remove any incorrect entries, where appropriate
- Post the correct entries

You do not need to give narratives.

Do NOT enter zeros into unused column cells.

Ignore VAT.

(a) Entries need to be made for an irrecoverable debt of £192.

Journal

	Dr £	Cr £

(b) A loan repayment of £1,300 has been made from the bank. The correct entry was made to the bank account but no other entries were made.

Journal

	Dr £	Cr £

(c) No entries have been made for closing stock for the year-end 31 March 20X1. Closing stock has been valued at cost at £18,500. Included in this figure are some items costing £1,250 that will be sold for £975.

Journal

	Dr £	Cr £

* *An alternative task about recording adjustments in the extended trial balance appears on page 119*

(d) The figures from the columns of the purchases day book for 23 March have been totalled correctly as follows:

Purchases column	£1,000
VAT column	£200
Total column	£1,200

The amounts have been posted as follows:

Dr Purchases	£1,000
Cr VAT	£200
Cr Purchases ledger control account	£1,200

Journal

	Dr £	Cr £

Task 2.2 *(alternative)*

This task is about recording adjustments in the extended trial balance and closing off accounts.

You are working on the final accounts of a business with a year-end of 31 March. A trial balance has been drawn up and a suspense account opened with a credit balance of £1,100. You now need to make some corrections and adjustments for the year ended 31 March 20X1.

(a) Record the adjustments needed on the extract from the extended trial balance to deal with the items below.

You will not need to enter adjustments on every line. Do NOT enter zeros into unused cells.

(i) Entries need to be made for an irrecoverable debt of £192.

(ii) A loan repayment of £1,300 has been made. The correct entry was made to the loan account but no other entries were made.

(iii) No entries have been made for closing stock for the year-end 31 March 20X1. Closing stock has been valued at cost at £18,500. Included in this figure are some items costing £1,250 that will be sold for £975.

(iv) The figures from the columns of the sales day book for 23 March have been totalled correctly as follows:

Sales column	£1,000
VAT column	£200
Total column	£1,200

The amounts have been posted as follows:

Cr Sales	£1,000
Cr VAT	£200
Dr Sales ledger control account	£1,000

Extract from extended trial balance

	Ledger balances		Adjustments	
	Dr £	Cr £	Dr £	Cr £
Allowance for doubtful debts		365		
Bank	4,300			
Closing stock – balance sheet				
Closing stock – P&L account				
Depreciation charge				
Irrecoverable debts				
Loan		4,000		
Loan interest	240			
Plant and machinery – accumulated depreciation		22,000		
Sales		210,000		
Sales ledger control account	24,500			
Suspense		1,100		
VAT		5,600		

(b) The ledgers are ready to be closed off for the year ended 31 March 20X1. Show the correct entries to close off the loan interest account and select an appropriate narrative.

Account	Dr ✓	Cr

Task 2.3

This task is about completing an extended trial balance.

You have the following extended trial balance. The adjustments have already been correctly entered.

Extend the figures into the profit and loss and balance sheet columns.

Do NOT enter zeros into unused column cells.

Make the columns balance by entering figures and a label in the correct places.

Extended trial balance

Ledger account	Ledger balances		Adjustments		Profit and loss account		Balance sheet	
	£ Dr	*£ Cr*	*£ Dr*	*£ Cr*	*£ Dr*	*£ Cr*	*£ Dr*	*£ Cr*
Allowance for doubtful debts		1,300	300					
Allowance for doubtful debts adjustment				300				
Bank	28,380			500				
Capital		4,530						
Closing stock			30,000	30,000				
Depreciation charge			15,500					
Office expenses	69,550			500				
Opening stock	26,000							
Payroll expenses	31,150			150				
Purchases	188,000		900					
Purchases ledger control account		29,900						
Sales		436,000						
Sales ledger control account	36,000							
Selling expenses	67,000							
Suspense		250	1,150	900				
VAT		9,800						
Vehicles at cost	62,000							
Vehicles accumulated depreciation		26,300		15,500				
Profit/loss for the year								
	508,080	508,080	47,850	47,850				

Task 2.4

This task is about preparing reconciliations.

The bank statement has been compared with the cash book and the following differences identified:

1. Bank interest paid of £62 was not entered in the cash book.
2. A cheque for £450 has been incorrectly entered in the cash book as £540.
3. Cheques totalling £2,980 paid into the bank at the end of the month are not showing on the bank statement.
4. A BACS receipt of £3,200 from a customer has not been entered in the cash book.

The balance showing on the bank statement is a credit of £4,628 and the balance in the cash book is a debit of £4,380.

Use the following table to show the THREE adjustments you need to make to the cash book.

Adjustment	Amount £	Debit ✓	Credit ✓

Note: alternatives to this task could include purchases or sales ledger control reconciliations.

Task 2.5

Choose ONE answer.

Subsidiary purchase ledger accounts are kept to:

		✓
(a)	Summarise the total purchases for the business	
(b)	Show how much suppliers are owed in total	
(c)	Show how much each individual supplier is owed	
(d)	Enable the production of individual customer statements	

Accounts preparation I

Practice assessment 3

Time allowance: 2 hours

- Each task of the Assessment is to be answered separately.
- The rate of Value Added Tax used is 20%.

Section 1

Task 1.1

This task is about recording information for non-current assets for a business known as Tyler Trading. Tyler Trading is registered for VAT and has a financial year end of 31 March.

The following is a purchase invoice received by Tyler Trading relating to some items to be used in its office:

To: Tyler Trading **Tyler House** **14 Blenheim Road** **Linton** **LT4 6AR**	**Invoice 7341** Copier Services Ltd 28 Booth Lane Burdish BD3 8AP		**Date:** **25 Nov 20X5** **Total £**
Multifunction copier	Model XPL417	1	650.00
Toner cartridge	XPL4 Blk/Col	2	90.00
Installation		1	50.00
First year service contract		1	60.00
Total			850.00
Delivery date: 25/11/20X5			

Tyler Trading paid £850.00 to Copier Services Ltd on 28 November 20X5 with £850.00 borrowed interest-free from a third party. This amount is to be repaid in full on 31 December 20X7.

The following information relates to the sale of a delivery van no longer required by the business:

Description	2.0 litre van VU13 ZUP
Date of sale	10 March 20X6
Selling price	£4,000.00

- VAT can be ignored
- Tyler Trading has a policy of capitalising expenditure over £500.
- Office equipment is depreciated at 30% per year on a straight-line basis.
- Motor vehicles are depreciated at 25% on a diminishing balance basis.
- A full year's depreciation is applied in the year of acquisition and none in the year of disposal.

Record the following in the extract from the non-current assets register on the next page:

(a) Any acquisitions of non-current assets during the year ended 31 March 20X6

(b) Any disposals of non-current assets during the year ended 31 March 20X6

(c) Depreciation for the year ended 31 March 20X6

Notes

- *Not every cell will require and entry*
- *Show your answers to two decimal places*

Extract from the non-current assets register

Description/ serial no	Acquisition date	Cost £	Depreciation charges £	Carrying amount £	Funding method	Disposal proceeds £	Disposal date
Office equipment							
Laptop computer PT4	16/06/X4	750.00			Cash		
Year end 31/03/X5			225.00	525.00			
Year end 31/03/X6							
Year end 31/03/X6							
Motor vehicles							
1.6 litre car VX63 PSX	20/09/X3	10,240.00			Part-exchange		
Year end 31/03/X4			2,560.00	7,680.00			
Year end 31/03/X5			1,920.00	5,760.00			
Year end 31/03/X6							
2.0 litre van VU13 ZUP	02/04/X3	9,600.00			Part-exchange		
Year end 31/03/X4			2,400.00	7,200.00			
Year end 31/03/X5			1,800.00	5,400.00			
Year end 31/03/X6							

Task 1.2

This task is about recording non-current asset information in the general ledger, and other non-current asset matters.

You are working on the accounts of a business for the year ended 31 March 20X6.

- VAT can be ignored.
- A machine was part-exchanged on 20 September 20X5.
- The original machine was bought for £6,700 on 10 August 20X1.
- Depreciation is provided at 15% per year on a straight-line basis.
- A full year's depreciation is applied in the year of acquisition and none in the year of disposal.
- A part-exchange allowance of £3,000 was given.
- £6,400 was paid from the bank to complete the purchase of the new machine.

Make entries relating to the disposal:

(a) Complete the disposals account

(b) Update the bank account

On each account, show clearly the balance carried down or transferred to the income statement account in the general ledger as appropriate.

Select your entries for the 'Details' column from the following list: Balance b/d, Balance c/d, Bank, Depreciation charges, Disposals, Income statement account, Machinery accumulated depreciation, Machinery at cost, Purchases, Purchases ledger control, Repair and maintenance costs, Sales, Sales ledger control.

Disposals

Details	£	Details	£

Bank

Details	**£**	**Details**	**£**
Balance b/d	15,365		

(c) Calculate the total cost of the new machine.

£

(d) What will be the carrying amount of the new machine as at 31 March 20X7?

£

Section 2

Task 2.1

This task is about accounting for accrued and prepaid income and expenses.

You are working on the accounts of a business for the year ended 31 March 20X6.

In this task, you can ignore VAT.

You have the following information:

- The balance on the rent receivable account at the beginning of the financial year is £2,400. This represents a prepayment for rent receivable as at the end of the year on 31/03/X5.
- The bank summary for the year shows receipts for rent receivable of £15,900.
- The rent receivable account has been correctly adjusted for £3,000 rent for the quarter ended 31 May 20X6, which was received into the bank on 28 March 20X6.
- Double entry accounting is done in the general ledger.

(a) Complete the following statements by calculating the required figure and selecting ONE option from each box.

On 01/04/X5, the rent receivable account shows a | DEBIT / CREDIT | balance of £ | |

On 31/03/X6, the rent receivable account shows an adjustment for

| ACCRUED EXPENSES / ACCRUED INCOME / PREPAID INCOME |

of | £ |

(b) Calculate the rent receivable for the year ended 31/03/X6.

| £ |

The bank summary for the year shows payments for electricity expenses of £6,475.

(c) Update the electricity expenses account for this, showing clearly the balance to be carried down.

Select your entries for the 'Details' column from the following list:

Accrued expenses, Accrued income, Balance b/d, Balance c/d, Bank, Electricity expenses, Income statement account, Prepaid expenses, Prepaid income, Purchases, Purchases ledger control, Rent receivable, Sales, Sales ledger control.

Electricity expenses

Details	**£**	**Details**	**£**
Balance b/d	135		

You now find out that there is an unpaid bill of £630 for electricity for the three months ended 30 April 20X6 that has not been included in the accounts.

(d) Complete the following statements by calculating the required figure and selecting ONE option from each box.

Adjusting for this will [INCREASE / DECREASE / HAVE NO EFFECT ON] the total electricity figure transferred to the income statement for the year.

The adjustment is [£]

Electricity will show as a [DEBIT / CREDIT] in the income statement account in the general ledger.

Task 2.2

This task is about preparing a trial balance.

You are working on the accounts of a business with a year end of 31 March. You have five extracts from the ledger accounts as at 31 March 20X6. You need to start preparing the trial balance as at 31 March 20X6.

Using all the information given below and the figures given in the table on the next page, enter amounts in the appropriate trial balance columns for the accounts shown.

Do NOT enter zeros in the unused column cells.

Do NOT enter any figures as negatives.

Bank

	Details	£		Details	£
31/3/X6	Balance b/f	4,724			

Disposal of non-current assets

	Details	£		Details	£
31/3/X6	Balance b/f	240			

Heating and lighting

	Details	£		Details	£
31/3/X6	Balance b/f	4,175			

This balance has been adjusted for accrued expenses of £220 as at 31/03/X6.

Rent receivable

	Details	£		Details	£
			31/3/X6	Balance b/f	3,290

This balance has been adjusted for prepaid income of £440 as at 31/03/X6.

VAT

	Details	£		Details	£
			31/3/X6	Balance b/f	1,840

Extract from the trial balance as at 31 March 20X6

Account	Ledger balance £	Trial balance £ Dr	£ Cr
Accrued expenses			
Bank			
Discounts received	865		
Disposal of non-current assets			
Drawings	10,840		
Heating and lighting			
Office equipment	15,250		
Prepaid income			
Rent receivable			
VAT			

There were no accruals or prepayments of expenses and income other than those stated.

Task 2.3

This task is about recording journal entries.

You are working on the accounts of a business with a year end of 31 March. A trial balance has been drawn up and a suspense account opened. You now need to make some corrections and adjustments for the year ended 31 March 20X6.

Record the journal entries needed in the general ledger to deal with the items below.

You should:

- remove any incorrect entries, where appropriate
- post the correct entries

You do not need to give narratives.

Do NOT enter zeros into unused column cells.

Select your entries for the 'Details' column from the following list: Accruals, Allowance for doubtful debts, Allowance for doubtful debts adjustment, Bank, Electricity expenses, Irrecoverable debts, Prepayments, Purchases, Purchases ledger control, Purchases returns, Sales, Sales ledger control, Sales returns, Suspense, VAT, Vehicles, Vehicle expenses.

(a) Vehicle expenses of £220 have been charged to the vehicles account in error. The other side of the entry was correct.

Journal

Details	Dr £	Cr £

(b) A direct debit payment for electricity expenses of £126 has been correctly recorded in the bank account. No other entry has been made. Ignore VAT.

Journal

Details	Dr £	Cr £

(c) **The allowance for doubtful debts needs to be adjusted to 3% of the outstanding trade receivables. The sales ledger control account has a balance of £25,400 at the year end. The balance on the allowance for doubtful debts account is £845.**

Journal

Details	**Dr** **£**	**Cr** **£**

(d) **The figures from the columns of the purchases returns day book for 31 March 20X6 have been totalled correctly as follows:**

Purchases returns column	£690
VAT column	£138
Total column	£828

The amounts have been posted as follows:

Dr Purchases ledger control	£828
Cr Purchases returns	£690
Cr VAT	£183

Journal

Details	**Dr** **£**	**Cr** **£**

Task 2.4

You have the following extended trial balance. The adjustments have already been correctly entered.

Extend the figures into the income statement and statement of financial position columns.

Do NOT enter zeros into unused column cells.

Make the columns balance by entering figures and a label in the correct places.

Extended trial balance

Ledger account	Ledger balances		Adjustments		Income statement		Statement of financial position	
	£ Dr	£ Cr	£ Dr	£ Cr	£ Dr	£ Cr	£ Dr	£ Cr
Accruals				230				
Bank	9,420		85					
Capital		35,000		10,500				
Closing inventory			9,450	9,450				
Depreciation charges	4,700							
Drawings			10,500					
General expenses	26,081			346				
Machinery at cost	23,500							
Machinery – accumulated depreciation		7,920						
Opening inventory	8,190							
Prepayments			346					
Purchases	58,484							
Purchases ledger control		7,368		247				
Rent receivable		2,765						
Sales		117,622						
Sales ledger control	13,378							
Suspense		162	247	85				
Wages	27,084		230					
Loss/Profit*								
TOTAL								

** delete as appropriate*

Task 2.5

This task is about preparing reconciliations.

The individual balances of the accounts in the purchases ledger have been listed and totalled to £22,360. The total has been compared with the £19,835 balance on the purchases ledger control account. After investigation the following errors were found:

1. Bank payments of £2,245 made to suppliers have not been recorded in the individual accounts.
2. A credit note received for £230 has been credited to the supplier's account.
3. A purchase invoice of £865 has been posted to Supplier X's account in the purchases ledger, rather than Supplier Y.
4. A supplier account with a credit balance of £1,640 has been listed in the purchases ledger as £1,460.

Use the following table to show the THREE adjustments required to the listing of purchases ledger balances.

Adjustment number	Amount £	Add ✓	Deduct ✓

Task 2.6

This task is to test your knowledge.

A business is expected to continue to trade in the foreseeable future, so the income statement and statement of financial position are prepared on the basis that there is no intention to reduce significantly the size of the business or to liquidate the business.

(a) Which ONE of the following accounting principles (concepts) best describes this rule of accounting?

	✔
Accruals	
Consistency	
Going concern	
Prudence	

(b) Which of these statements is true? (Choose ONE.)

	✔
Capital expenditure is expenditure incurred on the running expenses of a business.	
The cost of installation of a non-current asset can be included in the capital expenditure of that asset.	
The cost of repairs of a non-current asset can be included in the capital expenditure of that asset.	
Capital expenditure is shown on the income statement as an expense.	

Practice assessment answers

Accounts preparation I

Practice Assessment 1 page 138

Practice Assessment 2 page 144

Practice Assessment 3 page 149

1 Accounts preparation 1 Practice assessment – answers

Section 1: Accounting for non-current (fixed) assets

Task 1.1

NON-CURRENT ASSET REGISTER

Description/serial no	Acquisition date	Cost £	Depreciation £	Carrying amount £	Funding method	Disposal proceeds £	Disposal date
Computer equipment							
PHX Laser printer	15/12/X7	1,200.00			Cash		
Year end 31/03/X8			360.00	840.00			
Year end 31/03/X9			360.00	480.00			
Year end 31/03/X0			360.00	120.00			
PHX Laptop computer	26/03/X0	750.00			Cash		
Year end 31/03/X0			225.00	525.00			
Vehicles							
PT07 PZV	20/05/X7	16,000.00			Cash		
Year end 31/03/X8			4,000.00	12,000.00			
Year end 31/03/X9			3,000.00	9,000.00			
Year end 31/03/X0			–	–		7,500.00	14/03/X0
PT58 ZPE	19/11/X8	14,400.00			Part-exchange		
Year end 31/03/X9			3,600.00	10,800.00			
Year end 31/03/X0			2,700.00	8,100.00			

Tutorial note: the delivery cost of the laptop computer is capitalised.

Task 1.2

(a) **Machinery at cost**

Balance b/d	£25,000		
Bank	£6,000	Balance c/d	£31,000
	£31,000		£31,000

(b) **Machinery: accumulated depreciation**

		Balance b/d	£8,000
Balance c/d	£8,800	Depreciation charge	£800
	£8,800		£8,800

Machinery: depreciation charge

Balance b/d	£1,000	Income statement	£1,800
Machinery: accumulated depreciation	£800		
	£1,800		£1,800

(c)

It shows the carrying amount of each machine	✔

Section 2: Extending the trial balance using accounting adjustments

Task 2.1

(a) **Vehicle expenses**

	£		£
Bank	5,540	Balance b/d	300
		Income statement	4,720
		Balance c/d	520
	5,540		5,540

(b) **Selling expenses**

		£			£
20X0 1 Apr	Balance b/d	450	20X1 31 Mar	Income statement	12,390
20X1 31 Mar	Bank	11,650			
20X1 31 Mar	Balance c/d	290			
		12,390			12,390

(c)

Account	**£**	**£ Dr**	**£ Cr**
Accruals			290
Capital	40,000		40,000
Discount allowed	470	470	
Drawings	18,500	18,500	
Interest received	350		350
Office equipment at cost	15,000	15,000	
Office equipment: accumulated depreciation	6,500		6,500
Prepayments		520	

Task 2.2

(a) **Journal**

	Dr £	Cr £
Irrecoverable debts	150	
Sales ledger control		150

(b) **Journal**

	Dr £	Cr £
Rent	600	
Suspense		600

(c) **Journal**

	Dr £	Cr £
Closing inventory – statement of financial position	*17,780	
Closing inventory – income statement		*17,780

* lower of cost and net realisable value: £18,300 – £520

(d) **Journal**

	Dr £	Cr £
VAT	240	
Suspense		240
VAT	240	
Suspense		240

Task 2.3

Extended trial balance

Ledger account	Ledger balances		Adjustments		Income statement		Statement of financial position	
	£ Dr	£ Cr	£ Dr	£ Cr	£ Dr	£ Cr	£ Dr	£ Cr
Allowance for doubtful debts		2,100	250					1,850
Allowance for doubtful debts adjustment				250		250		
Bank	3,700			200			3,500	
Capital		40,000						40,000
Closing inventory			21,300	21,300		21,300	21,300	
Depreciation charge			2,750		2,750			
Machinery at cost	25,000						25,000	
Machinery: accumulated depreciation		11,500		2,750				14,250
Office expenses	7,350			300	7,050			
Opening inventory	19,100				19,100			
Payroll expenses	16,850		500		17,350			
Purchases	76,200				76,200			
Purchases ledger control		11,400						11,400
Sales		118,200	450			117,750		
Sales ledger control	30,950						30,950	
Selling expenses	5,750				5,750			
Suspense	450		500	950				
VAT		2,150						2,150
Profit/loss for the year					11,100			11,100
	185,350	185,350	25,750	25,750	139,300	139,300	80,750	80,750

Tutorial note: the debit balance of £450 on suspense account is cleared by the debit adjustment for £500 (£200 and £300), and the credit adjustment for £950 (£500 and £450).

Task 2.4

Adjustment number	Amount £	Debit ✓	Credit ✓
1	100	✓	
2	300		✓
4	150		✓

Task 2.5

(a)

consistency	✔

(b)

to gather and summarise accounting information for the double-entry system	✔

Accounts Preparation I
Answers to Assessment 2

SECTION 1: Accounting for non-current (fixed) assets

Task 1.1 Fixed assets register

Description	*Acquisition date*	*Cost £*	*Depreciation £*	*Net book value £*	*Funding method*	*Disposal proceeds*	*Disposal date*
Computer equipment							
Server main office	30/09/X7	2,800.00			Cash		
Year end 31/03/X8			840.00	1,960.00			
Year end 31/03/X9			840.00	1,120.00			
Year end 31/03/X0			840.00	280.00			
HP printer 65438LKR	28/03/X0	775.00			Cash		
Year end 31/03/X0			232.50	542.50			
Motor Vehicles							
AB08 DRF	01/04/X7	12,000.00			Cash		
Year end 31/03/X8			3,000.00	9,000.00			
Year end 31/03/X9			2,250.00	6,750.00			
Year end 31/03/X0			—	—		5,500.00	15/03/X0
AB07 FRP	31/01/X9	9,600.00			Part-exchange		
Year end 31/03/X9			2,400.00	7,200.00			
Year end 31/03/X0			1,800.00	5,400.00			

Task 1.2 **(a) and (b)**

Vehicles at cost

Balance b/d	10,000	Balance c/d	14,000
Bank	4,000		
	14,000		14,000

Vehicles accumulated depreciation

Balance c/d	3,625	Balance b/d	3,000
		Depreciation charge	625
	3,625		3,625

Depreciation charge

Balance b/d	1,000	Profit and loss account	1,625
Vehicles accumulated depreciation	625		
	1,625		1,625

(c) New vehicle purchases should be authorised by: (a) A partner of the business

Section 2 – Extending the trial balance using accounting adjustments

Task 2.1

(a)

Administration expenses

	£		£
Bank	6,190	Balance b/d	790
		Profit and loss account	4,200
		Balance c/d	1,200
	6,190		6,190

(b)

Selling expenses

		£			£
1/4	Bal b/d	375	31/3	Profit and loss account	9,100
31/3	Bank	7,900			
31/3	Bal c/d	825			
		9,100			9,100

(c)

Extract from trial balance as at 31 March 20X1

Account	£	*£ Dr*	*£ Cr*
Accruals			
Accruals			825
Capital	6,000		6,000
Depreciation charge	850	850	
Drawings	11,000	11,000	
Interest received	70		70
Machinery at cost	5,600	5,600	
Machinery accumulated depreciation	4,200		4,200
Prepayments		1,200	

Task 2.2

(a) Journal

	Dr £	Cr £
Irrecoverable debts	192	
Sales ledger control account		192

(b) Journal

	Dr £	Cr £
Loan	1,300	
Suspense		1,300

(c) Journal

	Dr £	Cr £
Closing stock – balance sheet	18,225	
Closing stock – profit and loss account		18,225

(d) Journal

	Dr £	Cr £
VAT	200	
Suspense		200
VAT	200	
Suspense		200

Task 2.2 *(alternative)*

(a) Extract from extended trial balance

	Ledger balances		*Adjustments*	
	Dr £	**Cr** £	**Dr** £	**Cr** £
Allowance for doubtful debts		365		
Bank	4,300			1,300
Closing stock – balance sheet			18,225	
Closing stock – P&L account				18,225
Depreciation charge				
Irrecoverable debts			192	
Loan		4,000		
Loan interest	240			
Plant and machinery – accumulated depreciation		22,000		
Sales		210,000		
Sales ledger control account	24,500		200	192
Suspense		1,100	1,300	200
VAT		5,600		

(b)

Account	**Dr**	**Cr**
Profit and loss account	✓	
Loan interest		✓
Transfer of loan interest for year ended 31 March 20X1 to profit and loss account		

Task 2.3

Extended trial balance

Ledger account	Ledger balances		Adjustments		Profit and loss account		Balance sheet	
	£ Dr	£ Cr	£ Dr	£ Cr	£ Dr	£ Cr	£ Dr	£ Cr
Allowance for doubtful debts		1,300	300					1,000
Allowance for doubtful debts adjustment				300		300		
Bank	28,380			500			27,880	
Capital		4,530						4,530
Closing stock			30,000	30,000		30,000	30,000	
Depreciation charge			15,500		15,500			
Office expenses	69,550			500	69,050			
Opening stock	26,000				26,000			
Payroll expenses	31,150			150	31,000			
Purchases	188,000		900		188,900			
Purchases ledger control account		29,900						29,900
Sales		436,000				436,000		
Sales ledger control account	36,000						36,000	
Selling expenses	67,000				67,000			
Suspense		250	1,150	900				
VAT		9,800						9,800
Vehicles at cost	62,000						62,000	
Vehicles accumulated depreciation		26,300		15,500				41,800
Profit/loss for the year					68,850			68,850
	508,080	508,080	47,850	47,850	466,300	466,300	155,880	155,880

Task 2.4

Adjustment	**Amount £**	**Debit ✓**	**Credit ✓**
Adjustment for 1	62		✓
Adjustment for 2	90	✓	
Adjustment for 4	3,200	✓	

Task 2.5

(c) Show how much each individual supplier is owed.

Accounts Preparation I
Answers to Assessment 3

Section 1

Task 1.1

Extract from the non-current assets register

Description/ serial no	Acquisition date	Cost £	Depreciation charges £	Carrying amount £	Funding method	Disposal proceeds £	Disposal date
Office equipment							
Laptop computer PT4	16/06/X4	750.00			Cash		
Year end 31/03/X5			225.00	525.00			
Year end 31/03/X6			225.00	300.00			
Copier XPL417	25/11/X5	700.00			Loan		
Year end 31/03/X6			210.00	490.00			
Motor vehicles							
1.6 litre car VX63 PSX	20/09/X3	10,240.00			Part-exchange		
Year end 31/03/X4			2,560.00	7,680.00			
Year end 31/03/X5			1,920.00	5,760.00			
Year end 31/03/X6			1,440.00	4,320.00			
2.0 litre van VU13 ZUP	02/04/X3	9,600.00			Part-exchange		
Year end 31/03/X4			2,400.00	7,200.00			
Year end 31/03/X5			1,800.00	5,400.00			
Year end 31/03/X6			nil	nil		4,000.00	10/03/X6

Tutorial note: the installation cost of the copier is capitalised.

Task 1.2

(a)

Disposals

Details	**£**	**Details**	**£**
Machinery at cost	6,700	Machinery accumulated depreciation	4,020
Income statement account	320	Machinery at cost	3,000
	7,020		7,020

(b)

Bank

Details	**£**	**Details**	**£**
Balance b/d	15,365	Machinery at cost	6,400
		Balance c/d	8,965
	15,365		15,365

(c) **£9,400** ie £3,000 + £6,400

(d) **£6,580** ie £9,400 – (£1,410 depreciation x 2 years)

Section 2

Task 2.1

(a) A CREDIT balance of £2,400

An adjustment for PREPAID INCOME of £3,000

(b) £15,300

(c)

Electricity expenses

Details	£	Details	£
Balance b/d	135	Balance c/d	6,610
Bank	6,475		
	6,610		6,610

(d) Adjusting for this will INCREASE the total electricity figure transferred to the income statement for the year.

The adjustment is £420

Electricity will show as a DEBIT in the income statment account in the general ledger.
Tutorial note: the adjustment is for February and March.

Task 2.2

Extract from the trial balance as at 31 March 20X6

	Ledger balance	Trial balance	
Account	£	£ Dr	£ Cr
Accrued expenses			220
Bank		4,724	
Discounts received	865		865
Disposal of non-current assets		240	
Drawings	10,840	10,840	
Heating and lighting		4,175	
Office equipment	15,250	15,250	
Prepaid income			440
Rent receivable			3,290
VAT			1,840

Task 2.3

(a)

Journal

Details	Dr £	Cr £
Vehicle expenses	220	
Vehicles		220

(b)

Journal

Details	Dr £	Cr £
Electricity expenses	126	
Suspense		126

(c)

Journal

Details	Dr £	Cr £
Allowance for doubtful debts	83	
Allowance for doubtful debts adjustment		83

(d)

Journal

Details	Dr £	Cr £
VAT	183	
Suspense		183
Suspense	138	
VAT		138

Task 2.4

Extended trial balance

Ledger account	Ledger balances		Adjustments		Income statement		Statement of financial position	
	£ Dr	£ Cr	£ Dr	£ Cr	£ Dr	£ Cr	£ Dr	£ Cr
Accruals				230				230
Bank	9,420		85				9,505	
Capital		35,000		10,500				45,500
Closing inventory			9,450	9,450		9,450	9,450	
Depreciation charges	4,700				4,700			
Drawings			10,500				10,500	
General expenses	26,081			346	25,735			
Machinery at cost	23,500						23,500	
Machinery – accumulated depreciation		7,920						7,920
Opening inventory	8,190				8,190			
Prepayments			346				346	
Purchases	58,484				58,484			
Purchases ledger control		7,368		247				7,615
Rent receivable		2,765				2,765		
Sales		117,622				117,622		
Sales ledger control	13,378						13,378	
Suspense		162	247	85				
Wages	27,084		230		27,314			
Profit					5,414			5,414
TOTAL	170,837	170,837	20,858	20,858	129,837	129,837	66,679	66,679

Tutorial note: the credit balance of £162 on suspense account is cleared by the debit adjustment for £247 and the credit adjustment for £85.

Task 2.5

Adjustment number	**Amount £**	**Add ✓**	**Deduct ✓**
1	2,245		✓
2	460		✓
4	180	✓	

Task 2.6

(a) Going concern

(b) The cost of installation of a non-current asset can be included in the capital expenditure of that asset.